TILTING

NICOLE HARKIN

BLACK ROSE
writing™

ISBN: 978-1-61296-892-6
PUBLISHED BY BLACK ROSE WRITING
www.blackrosewriting.com

Printed in the United States of America
Suggested Retail Price (SRP) $18.95

Tilting is printed in Adobe Caslon Pro
Cover design by Ivan Bjørn with NadaVisual.com

To Oskar, Otis, and Brent.

And John, Erica, Montana, Gram, and Walt.

Praise for *TILTING*

"The way Nicole wrote this book - so honest and relatable, straight to the point and real - gave me pause to think about how we face life. She manages to find compassion, wisdom and humor in the depths of pain and the end of everything she knew."

- Sonia Voldseth, Life Coach/Owner at Revolutionary Life Coaching and Sometimes Blogger

"*Tilting* is instantly relatable, yet a story only Nicole Harkin could tell, weaving details that set you definitively in the era and setting. *Tilting* tells of both the rite of passage experiences all kids have with the life changing devastations only the author has experienced, which makes for a story that hurts your heart and also makes your heart sing."

- Jennifer Fliss, Writer

TILTING

A new day is upon us,

A day of wonder,

A year of promise,

A lifetime of hope.

~ Mary DeTurris Poust ~

1996, Montana

DAD piloted one of the last planes into the downtown Hong Kong airport before the airport relocated. This had him flying a jumbo jet between high-rises right through the city. People in the apartments could see the pilots and wave. Autopilot wasn't an option. To land safely the pilot needed to manually steer the aircraft during landing and the approach challenged even the most seasoned pilot, but Dad liked flying into Hong Kong.

Dad came home from this, his first trip of the year, on a Tuesday. He told Linda he didn't feel well. Uncharacteristically, he headed to the doctor who told him he had a virus and needed to take some antibiotics. He would feel better after he rested.

I'd just returned to college after Christmas break. I called home that day and demanded to talk to Dad because the tires on the Suburban were almost bald.

"He's sick in bed. Can it wait?" asked Linda, my mom.

The snow was piled up high in Indiana where I went to college.

"Sick? In bed? Put him on the phone. It can't be that bad."

"He's very sick."

"Come on, Linda."

I didn't believe her. He just didn't want to give me any money. Money remained a constant struggle between us. My parents were always telling me they didn't have any money even though my father worked as an international airline pilot.

"Dad, hello? Are you there? Can you hear me?" I asked.

"What do ya need?" His Boston accent came out because he was annoyed that I had insisted on talking to him.

"The Suburban needs new tires."

"I don't feel well."

"Dad, it's icy here, and I'm sliding all over the place."

"Fine, get some new tires."

1983, Georgia

THIS year on vacation my family drove to a pontoon boat sitting on the Tennessee River. Dad had bought the boat sight unseen from a Penny Saver—a newspaper listing items for sale locally—he ran across while competing in a bass fishing tournament. He had planned to have us drive the boat up the river back home to Georgia.

Rarely were we in the car together. Because of his job as an airline pilot, Dad left for days or weeks at a time. When he was home he always drove faster than Linda wanted. As a precaution, Linda pressed an imaginary brake pedal on her side of the car.

When Dad went to pass another car, Linda sucked air and gulped, "Uuuuuhhhhhh, Jack, stop," while placing her hand on his arm.

She sucked air a lot when Dad drove, so we children sucked air as well and made up a song to the tune of "Stop in the Name of Love:"

"Uuuuuhhhhhh, Jack, Stop in the Name of Love,

Before you kill your children.

Think it ooohhhhhh over."

We even added hand motions and sang it in a three-part round. Through his chuckles, Dad said, "Kids, stop harassing your mother."

The frigid car contrasted with the overwhelming heat outside. *The Mamas and the Papas* played on repeat. Dad had bought the tape on our last road trip in Maine because he loved the band. At first the music had seemed cool.

As the gray station wagon with wood paneling barreled down the road, we saw the kudzu. It grew everywhere, taking over everything and making it green. Linda said the imported Japanese vine grew a foot a night and no one knew what to do about it. Linda sat next to Dad and smoked Benson & Hedges 100's from the gold pack. Dad smoked Marlboro Lights. I had to know the correct kind of cigarettes because I often had to run into the convenience store to buy them. Everyone smoked it seemed.

The three of us kids sat side by side, belted into place, happy for the warmth of the person next to us as our legs stuck to the Naugahyde seats. Then, when it was clear my parents weren't looking, my three-year-old younger sister, Erica attacked and pinched me on the arm. I hit back. Pandemonium ensued as Erica elbowed four-year-old John while hitting me in return.

"Knock it off!" yelled Dad.

I scowled at Erica. She smirked.

After hours of this same scene with the now hated music looping over and over, we arrived at the marina where the pontoon boat awaited us. The place smelled of fuel and dead fish. The hot pavement burned my eight-year-old feet, even through my shoes. After hitching the "new" pontoon boat to the back of the station wagon, we drove down to the river.

"Kids, what do you think of Cream Puff the 2nd?" Dad asked.

Dad had owned Cream Puff the 1st, a Jeep Wrangler, before he had a family.

"The boat looks like a wood pallet on top of two paper towel rolls," I said. He ignored my comment.

The previous owner of Cream Puff the boat had built it himself and made the pontoons out of steel rather than lighter aluminum.

The plan was to pilot this new-to-us, yet used boat up the river towards our home on Lake Lanier. Over the course of a week, we would see the country by boat. We would stay at marinas while stocking up on food there too as the trip progressed.

As mosquitoes swarmed around us, Dad backed the boat down the concrete ramp into the dirty brown Tennessee River.

"Kids, get over here. I've got the bug spray," said Linda, lipstick-stained cigarette in hand.

We lined up, always oldest to youngest because I had to assert my superiority over Erica and John.

As she sprayed us, I imagined the emergency brake not holding on the car, and then watching the boat and car slide into the water together. I thought this every time someone put a boat in the water. I willed it to occur. I wanted to see what would happen after that.

Once the boat—silver with an orange canopy and orange vinyl seats—had been backed into the water, Dad, in cutoff jeans and a plaid polyester short-sleeve shirt, got out and unhooked the boat. His wire-rimmed Ray-bans kept sliding down his nose. He looked less like William Shatner and more like Fred Flintstone as the sweat poured off his head. Water lapped at the station wagon's back tires.

Dad lugged the red cooler onto the boat.

"Nicole, go get more ice for the cooler."

"I thought we had ice," I said.

"Just go get the ice."

Linda gave me two dollars. In my rainbow-striped swimming suit and shorts, I trudged back up to the marina to get the ice.

Dad had loaded everything else onto the boat: the towels, including my favorite towel, a giant replica of a $100 bill, grocery bags of chips and juice boxes, and two cartons of cigarettes. I spied some Oreo cookies in the bags. Linda never let us have sugary treats.

"Everyone go to the bathroom," Linda said.

"I already went," I said.

"Nicole, take Erica and John to the bathroom," Linda said.

"I just got back from the marina. I don't want to go back up the hill," I said.

"We don't want to go with her," said Erica.

"I don't have to go to the bathroom, Mom," said John.

"Get going."

I sighed and grabbed the hands of the kids and went up the hill. When we returned to the boat, everyone piled in.

"Put on your life vests, kids," Linda said.

"I know how to swim," I said.

"You need to set an example for the kids," she replied.

Unable to put their arms down by their sides in their life vests, Erica and John looked like baby penguins.

"Where are we going?" I asked.

Dad showed me a map with squiggles on it.

"These lines tell you the topography of the river. The closer the lines, the steeper the riverbank. See how most of the marinas are near lines that aren't close together?" he explained.

As we motored up the river, John and Erica watched for the items on the map to appear in view.

"Here comes another marina," I said.

The most exciting river attractions were those that weren't found on the map: the houses, the birds, the animals. We floated by the next marina without stopping, which seemed strange. Linda and Dad had exchanged words, but I had missed what they said.

"Jack, look at that house," said Linda.

"Huh. We could tear down the garage and expand it," said Dad.

Linda and Dad house-hunted as a pastime.

John, with his curly red hair and blue eyes behind scratched glasses, kept up a running conversation whether anyone listened or not. We tuned him out and only popped to attention when he yelled.

"John, keep it down," said Dad.

"But look at that eagle, Dad!"

"It's a hawk."

"Oh, well, it's a big bird."

Erica sat on the flat part of the boat, under the canopy, looking angelic with long blond hair. Her fair skin always burned if Linda didn't constantly keep fresh sunscreen on the kid.

We made great time on the first day of the trip and didn't stop at any marinas. We ate the peanut butter and jelly or ham sandwiches Linda brought and drank the juice boxes.

"Mom, where are we stopping tonight? Can you show me on the map?"

Both parents looked at me but didn't say anything.

"Mom, the hotel is where on the map?"

"A hotel has different floors. A motel is only one floor. The places along the river are motels," Linda said.

"OK, where's the motel we're stopping at?"

"We're sleeping on the boat tonight."

I stared at Linda, thinking about what she said.

"But there's no place to go to the bathroom. Why?"

"Dad doesn't know where the money is," she said.

"It's in his wallet."

"Nicole, he doesn't know where his wallet is."

"Did he lose it?"

Again my parents looked back at me.

"He might have left it in the car," said Linda.

The boat with its orange cushions and orange all-weather carpet shrank. The party barge quickly lost its fun.

"Well, we have to go back."

1996, Montana

MY Uncle Frankie, Dad's older brother, picked me up at the airport. He and his wife lived a four-hour drive away in Washington State, but we rarely saw them. Because Frankie was naturally a gruff person, I couldn't get a read from him about the situation, other than to know it didn't look good for my father's survival. He told me that a helicopter had airlifted Dad in a snowstorm from Kalispell, Montana, to Missoula, Montana, one hundred and twenty miles away, because the hospital was better equipped to care for him. The doctors still didn't know what was wrong, but they knew his heart was failing.

After Dad had arrived they operated on his heart and replaced his heart valve.

I found my entire family in the waiting room. Everyone stood up and hugged me. The kid's eyes were red from crying. Crosses hung on the walls since it was a Catholic hospital and there was always a priest on duty roaming the halls. The room had fluorescent lights and uncomfortable chairs with bentwood arms covered in teal and peach cloth that looked to have last been cleaned twenty years earlier.

"What's wrong with Dad?" I asked Linda.

"They said he has some kind of bacteria in his blood—not a virus—and the bacteria isn't responding to antibiotics. He possibly picked up the infection on his last trip, or from picking his nose, or he just got it. They just don't know," said Linda.

She hadn't meant to be flippant, but she could be counted on tell the truth immediately. She didn't beat around the bush, even with her children and painful truths.

"They're sending samples of his blood to the CDC to get their help."

"But how long'll that take?" I asked.

"I don't know, Nicole."

We passed the time playing gin rummy. Uncle Frankie taught us how.

Periodically we checked in at the nurse's station. It wasn't clear what we were waiting for. Conversation lagged. We didn't have enough to say to each other.

Walking into Dad's room for the first time felt like Easter because of the colors of everything. The head of his bed abutted the wall and there was a chair on the side of his bed next to the window. Real curtains hung from the windows. Up to this point in my life, I had only been in a hospital once and I didn't know anyone who had been in the ICU. I had briefly visited Linda when she had my youngest brother Montana, but that was more than a decade earlier.

Seeing Dad shocked me. He was puffy and the respirator breathed for him, forcing his chest up and down at a constant rate. There were cords and tubing on his arms, torso, and face. Drains came out of incisions and other unmentionable areas. I saw the staples from his heart surgery on his black and blue chest when the nurses changed his gown. His eyelids flittered sometimes. The room smelled of antiseptic and stale air.

"Go ahead and talk to him. He may be able to hear you," said the nurse.

"Hi, Dad. It's me, Nicole. We are all here. We want you to get better," I said.

Then silence. I looked up at the heart monitor. Back to the IV. Then down at his hand that I held.

"You've had a rough week. But don't give up."

More silence.

The next morning a doctor came by for a family meeting.

"Your father has a staph infection that is attacking his body. We know the infection attacked his heart, which is why we had to replace his heart valve. The infected valve also sprayed infection throughout his body with every heartbeat. The infection caused him to have mini-strokes. This is why we decided to put him into a coma. Unfortunately, his body isn't responding to the antibiotics and he is experiencing a total system shutdown. His liver is beginning to fail."

"Total system shutdown" sounded like something that happened to a computer, I thought. But here it meant that his organs were failing in unison. As his systems failed one after another in a cascading effect, the liver remained as the lynchpin. If his liver failed, the only thing that could save him would be a liver transplant. But he couldn't get a liver transplant if the rest of his body was failing. He had two kidneys, so there was some redundancy there, even if one failed. The doctors had fixed his heart, so that was no longer an issue. His lungs could rest on the respirator. His brain remained a big question mark, but at that point, his liver function needed to improve in order for him to survive.

Even when he wasn't home, Dad remained a larger than life presence in our family. We all wanted to please him. He was a great thinker and he read voraciously. Between science fiction novels and Lee Iacocca's autobiography, there wasn't much he missed. Our home library was full of hardcover books, *National Geographics*, and encyclopedias.

My father's given name was John but he went by Jack. Born in Boston, he had mostly lost his accent unless I was in trouble and he was speaking quickly.

"You're nadasposta do that!"

People were attracted to him, his magnetism, and he exuded fun. He had that sense of competence that comes from being a pilot so that it always seemed like he knew what he was doing. Oftentimes it was only afterward that it occurred to people he might have been bluffing.

And while he worked hard, he was ever on the look out for a scheme to make him super rich, which was how he had ended up owning, at different times, a gliderport, a marina, and a bar in Montana. Other people wanted to be part of his schemes and in his orbit.

And he loved to go fast—be it flying, driving, skiing, or sailing. He had the chance to race in the America's Cup, the long-running international sailboat race, with Ted Turner before I was born. But Delta hadn't given him the time off from flying.

I wanted in on it all. I wanted to be with Dad any chance I had. I wanted to go fast, and do crazy things, and laugh hard. However, fundamentally I always only wanted one thing: for him to love me as much as I loved him.

Just a few days earlier he had been completely healthy. Then he had been a bit sick, but people get sick so it wasn't a big deal. Then as the situation escalated and hearts were opened and helicopters were flowing through snowstorms, I realized the gravity of the situation. The biggest question we had for the doctor was whether or not he would live. Would he die?

"We just don't know. He seems to have what we are beginning to think of as 'super bugs' that we can't control with penicillin. We'll have to wait and see, but it doesn't look good. The drug-induced coma should allow his body to rest and heal. When we feel he is ready we will try to take him out of the coma."

The doctor left the waiting room and we sat there stunned. The same things kept running through my head: Why me? Why him? Why now? Couldn't they fix him? How could this have happened?

We were all in shock.

His illness came on so suddenly that we didn't expect it to last long. We thought this was to be more of a freak storm after which everything would dry out and return to normal. But that's not what happened.

As the days of waiting turned into weeks, our lives took on a new rhythm. I took a leave of absence from college. This new rhythm meant me shuttling between Kalispell and Missoula, staying with friends when I was in Missoula. The kids and Linda stayed in Kalispell.

The days were spent with the nurses. The doctors came by once a day, in the early morning. If I wasn't there then, I couldn't ask them any questions, so I arrived early. The nurses had twelve-hour shifts. After the initial meet and greet, things settled into a routine. Within the first few minutes, I got a feel for the nurse and whether or not I liked his or her bedside manner. However, when someone's in a coma, how much bedside manner is needed?

At first, when something beeped, I ran out of the room to get the nurse. They congregated at the nurse's station behind a counter that kept the patient's families from getting too close. But I learned quickly only to rush out to get a nurse for actual problems, not merely beeping machines. Was there something physically wrong with Dad? Was he choking? Having problems breathing? Turning red? Or blue?

The nurses responded at differing rates. Some came running in. Some told me they were coming in a minute. Some were annoyed to have such an involved and assertive family member around. Standing behind that counter pleading with a nurse, any nurse, as Dad choked on the intubation tube and tried to pull it out, my desperation increased.

"Excuse me, my Dad's having a problem."

Slowly the female nurse turned around on her stool.

"Who's your Dad?"

"Jack Harkin. He's in this room."

"I'll get to it."

"Well, I think you need to come now."

No response.

"Please? He's choking."

But if honey didn't work, I became panicked and angry. If I had a nurse I trusted for the day, then I wouldn't get quite as agitated. But if I felt the nurse was incompetent—took too long to respond, made him wait too long for pain medicine, or didn't turn him regularly so he wouldn't get bedsores— then I shook and felt my blood pressure rise.

Soon I understood what the machines were for: measuring his blood pressure, delivering his medicine, helping him to breathe, etc. Compression pillows around his legs helped keep away bedsores. I also learned how to make the machines stop beeping. Many had a mute button.

Mostly he lay there, though. I held his hand. I put lotion on his arms and legs. I looked out the window. I went to get a soda. I talked to him, telling him about work, the kids, life. I chatted on the phone in the room. I waited alone. Me and Dad.

Dad's doctors decided to take Dad out of the coma. They reduced the medications keeping him asleep. He didn't wake up right away, though, so the doctors performed a brain scan. They wheeled a machine the size of a Ping-Pong table into his hospital room and hooked electrodes to his head. Much like an EKG for the heart, a little printout scrolled out of the machine onto the floor.

The electrodes on his head didn't detect any brain activity. They repeated the test every few days to see if there was any change. Looking over their shoulders, I could see the lines on the printouts were flat.

He was pronounced brain-dead three times. After the third time, the doctors started talking to Linda about removing Dad from life-support.

1982, Georgia

THE pontoon boat just appeared at our house on Lake Lanier, in Georgia, in the way that things just happen without any knowledge of how they happened when you are a child. We lived in a two-bedroom summer cottage on the lake fifty miles from downtown Atlanta in the middle of nowhere.

Linda had agreed to move to the "hovel" just before the pontoon boat trip in exchange for Dad's promise of a new house to be built next door.

In our old large house—named "River Run"—near downtown Atlanta, Gram, Linda's mother, had lived with us. She was my nanny when Linda and Dad were flying. I sat in Gram's room every day while she took hours to get ready. Gram wore a dark-brown hairpiece that went to her shoulders and flipped up, teased to maximum fullness. The large, mid-century home with a wraparound deck had a long driveway perfect for riding down in my red wagon while Gram sat behind me steering. Gram told almost everyone the house had twenty-four and a half rooms, which was a lot to vacuum. She also mentioned the house was made of fifty tons of stone. River Run was as far as one could get from my father's childhood outside of Boston. The weather was different, the accents were different, and he had money for clothing and food to spare.

While we lived at River Run, Linda still worked as a flight attendant for Delta. Gram and I could fly for free and went on trips to Disneyland and Disney World and to St. Louis to see her friends. I listened to Gram. I minded her.

"Nicole, what are you doing?"

I heard Gram call out to me as I sat poised in front of the little white vanity in my bedroom ready to cut off a chunk of my chestnut brown hair. How could she know what I was up to?

"Nothing."

"Nicole put the scissors down."

"Gram, how do you always know what I'm doing?"

"I have eyes on the back of my head, Nicole."

We played a lot of solitaire, but together. She had a glass coffee table and I sat under the table telling her which cards were where. Every morning we ate toast in her bed and watched *Phil Donahue* followed by *The Price Is Right*.

I loved our two big fluffy brown and white St. Bernard's, Killer and Geraldine. They were technically Dad's, but since he was a pilot and thus never home, Gram took care of them. They got into everything.

River Run was the first house my father lost. He spent too much money and instead of ratcheting back his spending, he filed for bankruptcy. He had lied on his mortgage application so he did not receive any bankruptcy protection. We lost the house. And we were, therefore, looking for a much smaller home. Unfortunately, when we moved to the hovel, Gram left me and moved into an apartment in the city. I also lost my dogs. Geraldine and Killer went to live with some St. Bernard loving friends of ours.

"I don't want to share my room with John," I emphatically told my parents when I realized that I would have to share my bedroom with my brother.

"Nicole, there are only two bedrooms. That's the deal. Kids in the one room and Mom and Dad in the other room," Linda said.

When we moved in, Linda put up yellow eyelet curtains in the two high windows above the twin beds. Matching yellow bedspreads were on the beds. When Erica arrived her crib was put at the foot of John's bed, and the changing table sat just outside our bedroom next to the kitchen.

To take Gram's place, Gram made me a giant denim doll named Sweet Pea that stood as tall as me and was super soft. Sweet Pea had large, white and blue embroidered eyes, perfect pink lips, and strands of denim hair. Sweet Pea and I were inseparable.

The hovel sat on a cul-de-sac at the end of a long road. Because there was rarely any traffic I spent hours circling and circling the loop on my too big bicycle, alone. Most of the neighbors didn't have kids.

I had a huge yard to play in that reached all the way down to the lake, but I was never ever allowed to go near the water unless an adult was with me. Linda had drilled that rule into me. In the concrete driveway which had a significant grade to it, sat Dad's beloved, royal blue 79' Corvette.

"Say 'goodbye' to the Corvette, Nicole."

"Bye!" I said brightly, not truly understanding what he meant.

He came home later that day with a giant brand-new blue Chevy truck. I thought that was the worst exchange in cars ever. Clearly the Corvette was way cooler than the truck. I cried, begging him to go get our blue racecar back.

The parking spots faced the lake. At the edge of the driveway a small divot in the concrete allowed rainwater to flow into a culvert fifteen feet below. This was the one place where a wheeled toy could go over the edge.

"John, will you push me in the wagon?" I asked.

He came running over with dirty hands and red curls ready to please. I sat in the wagon steering it as he pushed me.

"It's my turn, Nicole."

"Ok, just push me a little more."

Could he hear in my voice that I would never push him?

He kept pushing.

"OK, it's my turn now," said John.

"Just a little longer."

Having him push was fun. I liked driving. I kept putting him off.

"No, now."

"OK, how about you push me over there? Then we can switch," I said.

We moved closer to the edge of the driveway.

"Now it's my turn. It's not fair."

"Just a little further, John."

The wagon started moving faster and faster.

"John, STOP. Stop pushing! I'm about to go over the edge," I screamed.

He didn't stop and the wagon threaded the small divot sending me and the wagon over the edge. I laid there for some amount of time with one leg in the culvert and the other out, my privates hurting, yelling for help. No one came to help me, so I crawled up to the house. Linda never discussed what happened, too scared to even entertain what could have happened. That week a fence was put up around the driveway, so it couldn't happen again.

Lying in bed one night, I did some calculations: "John's almost five years younger than me. When he goes to first grade, I will be in fifth grade. After that, I won't ever have to go to the same school with him again. No one will have to know we're related."

Until I was five, I had been the only child, and from only to favorite wasn't a big leap. John and Erica had come along in short succession, eighteen months apart, ruining everything. I didn't like the kids for an amalgamation of reasons. To play with them would have been tacit admittance that I was, in fact, one of them. They were dirty and too small to do anything fun. They were slow. They always told on me if I broke the rules. They represented the loss of attention from my parents. But I wasn't above treating them like my slaves, having them push me in wagons and such.

1983, Georgia

YEARS earlier my little eight-year-old self walked down the linoleum-lined grocery aisle behind my mother. Everyone always noticed my mother. She stood almost six feet tall, a skinny, post-war child. She was "born blonde" once a month and had blue eyes the color of sweet pea flowers. Her fingernails were always done to perfection: chip-less red.

As we walked, a red spot grew on the back of her blue-striped dropped-waist summer dress. At first, I thought she had been hurt, had somehow been stabbed and was bleeding to death. But she seemed fine.

"Mom?"

No response.

"Mom."

Still no response.

"MOM!" I said in a loud whisper.

"Mother, please look at me?"

"Mom, come on. Please?"

Frustrated, I changed tactics. "Lin, Linda!"

She responded. I'd recently discovered that if I used her given name she responded faster. I pretended to be someone other than her daughter, another adult for her to chat with.

From then on I frequently called Linda by her first name instead of mom. I related to her as a fellow adult. My younger siblings were collectively, "the kids." This change in how I referred to her framed our entire relationship. I saw her as my equal. I felt we were both "parents." Most of the time, this helped Linda. But sometimes it drove her batty.

"There's something on the back of your dress."

"What is it, Nicole? Why are you whispering?"

"Because look at what it is," I said.

Linda twisted around to look at the back of her dress. With a shrug, she scooped up the spot on her dress in one hand and walked on clutching the

1984, Montana

DAD loved the West. He loved the clothes. He loved the ethos. We lived in Georgia because that's where his job as a pilot was based. Thus my parents deciding to send me to camp out West and eventually spending the summer in Bozeman, Montana wasn't surprising.

The apartments where we lived that summer in Bozeman were called the "bird houses" because they were gray and each had a different color trim. I was at Girl Scout camp most of the time, but Linda and the kids spent the summer visiting the Lewis and Clark Caverns, careening down the underground slides, and visiting the ghost towns that dotted the state. When Dad wasn't working, he flew out to Montana.

Erica came running inside one day, her long blond hair in knots down her back. She refused to let anyone brush it. And Dad refused to let anyone cut it.

"Mommy, there's a cow with wings outside."

"What, Erica?" she asked.

"Come quick, come quick. There's a cow with wings. It's going to get us."

Linda was busy and didn't run right outside.

"Mommy, please. The cow has wings."

Erica was sufficiently convincing that we finally went outside to see this cow with wings.

It was a bull with great big horns. I could understand her fear.

"They're not wings, they're horns!" I said.

"It had something like wings," said Erica.

At this point, John and Erica were out of diapers and could play by themselves. Soon, Erica would go to school, too, and Linda's days would be free.

But then things changed, a surprise.

After our summer out West, back in Georgia, our mornings played out the same way most of the time.

"Nicole get up. The bus will be here soon."

"Linda, I need help unrolling my hair," I said.

Sleeping on the pink curlers annoyed me, but my light-brown hair was so thin that without the curlers my hair lay flat on my head. In the South, a girl without big hair was marked as an outsider, a Yankee. Even though I was born in Atlanta, my parent's weren't from the South, and that counted against me. Once the pink curlers were out my hair looked slightly fuller.

In the upstairs bathroom, Linda hurriedly helped me with my hair. A cup of coffee with half-and-half sat precariously on the white porcelain sink.

Looking in the mirror I could see I was Dad's mini-me. We had the same brown hair. I had his dark-brown eyes and his big eyebrows. I laughed like him. And when I worked on something, I stared intently, blocking everything else out, just like he did.

I could never get Linda to admit that I was her favorite, but I kept trying. Often I would ask her, "Mom, who's your favorite kid?"

Sincerely, "You are."

"Really?"

"Yes."

Off I ran, feeling warm and fuzzy and extra special, to tell the other kids, "I'm Mom's favorite." Back to Linda everyone ran.

"Mom, am I your favorite or is Nicole?" asked Erica.

"You are."

"But she said she was?"

"You're all my favorite urchins."

"Mom, that's not fair," I said.

She just smiled at me.

When Dad asked me, "Do you want to come with me?" I felt like his favorite. He had chosen me to come with him on his errands.

"Where are you going?"

Most of the time going with him was boring. We drove and drove and then stopped and waited and waited. A lot of waiting in the car for him to come out of the store.

"Muppet, do you want to come or not?"

Dad called me by a few nicknames. Nickel, Rug Rat, and Muppet.

I loved him calling me Muppet.

"If I go with you can we get a treat?"

Sometimes he would stop and get chocolate stars to eat or a chocolate malt someplace.

"Maybe."

Anytime I asked Dad for something or to go somewhere and he answered with "maybe," he meant "no."

"That's not fair. I want to know."

"Life isn't fair. Do you want to come or not?" That was a refrain of his, "Life isn't fair." Don't expect life to be fair.

I joined him just in case. I wanted both, a treat and to spend time with him. I wanted to be the favorite.

That morning, back in the bathroom, I said to Linda, "Hurry up, I'm going to miss the bus."

We were always running late with me about to miss the school bus.

"Nicole, just wait for the curling iron to warm up."

Standing there in that tight space for a few quiet moments, I looked at Linda's waist in the mirror.

"Linda, you're starting to look a little fat. You either need to stop eating so much or you're pregnant."

Looking back at me in the mirror, her arm resting on my shoulder, Linda said, "I've been meaning to talk to you about that."

My eyes got very big. "What? You're pregnant again? Where will another baby sleep? You're too old to have another baby."

Linda was forty at the time. Dad forty-five.

"Let's get your hair done so you can catch the bus."

As I rode the yellow bus for forty-five minutes to Sugar Hill Elementary, I seethed. I didn't want another sibling.

I usually liked seeing out the front window and watching Mr. Tate, a grandfatherly older man, drive my bus to school. I counted the yellow dashes on the road as we drove, thinking. As I considered another sibling more, I realized this might be an opportunity. Erica and John hated me as much as I hated them. Maybe if I was nice to this new kid I might find an ally. Then it would be two against two.

I planned it out. With my youngest sibling I would take extra care and make the extra effort. I would change this baby's diapers. I would warm this baby's milk. I would take this baby on walks. I would teach this baby things. I would love it. This one would be my favorite, if only because it was the only one who liked me.

Linda and my new baby brother, George Montana, were at the hospital for such a long time that they finally let me go visit them there. John and Erica were too young to go. Gram took me in her black two-door Regal Buick. After Linda had Montana, as we called him, the doctors had removed part of her thyroid for some reason. That's why she had to stay longer. I had worried she was never coming back. But then she was home.

However, our baby, little Montana, was a bit yellow, jaundiced. The doctors said he had to sit on the screened porch every day for a few hours. He lay there googoo-gagaing. I would watch him for a bit and then move on to playing.

"Linda, there's a bee flying around Montana. What should I do?"

"Nothing, he's fine."

"What if it stings him?"

"It won't."

I stared at him with rapt attention. Why wasn't she worried, I wondered? How did she know nothing would happen to him?

After a few weeks, his skin was no longer jaundiced and he didn't have to lie outside anymore. He hadn't been stung.

Instead of retrenching into life with a baby, we just took Montana with us wherever we went, be it to soccer games, dance recitals, school plays, or church. Our lives didn't bend to his schedule, he adapted to ours.

1985, Georgia

WHEN Linda moved to the "hovel," she had extracted a promise from Dad to build the new house in the empty lot next to ours. For years the promised new house sat next to our hovel, unfinished. The architect had designed the house to look like a ship, with a tall peak in the middle of large glass windows that faced the lake. Around the outside of the second floor was a gigantic deck. The large sandstone fireplace at the back of the living room was visible from the lake and divided the living room from the kitchen. The new house seemed to be finished. Dad had "worked" on the house for three years.

Linda casually asked Dad one day when the new house would be ready for us to move into. I listened as their conversation unfolded because I could hear the strain in Linda's voice.

"Soon," he replied.

"Soon? We need more room. There is a perfectly good house sitting next door."

"Look, we can talk about it after my trip."

As soon as he left for the trip, Linda called Walt.

"We're moving this weekend," she told him.

Walt lived in Atlanta and worked as a machinist for Delta Air Lines. He acted as a kind of emissary from the city. When Linda needed shrimp or lime chutney, Walt found it for her. Sometimes he brought baby chicken legs for dinner. They later turned out to be frog legs. He clipped articles from the *Wall Street Journal*—which he read daily before his shift at Delta—for Linda to read.

"You want to move into the new house?" Walt asked.

"Yes, the new house. It's finished enough. I think Jack wants to sell it instead of moving us into it. After work, get out here and bring boxes," she said.

Walt arrived that weekend with wine and boxes. He came almost every weekend and slept on the brown, velvet couch downstairs in the hovel.

Walt and Linda worked as a team to raise me and the kids while Dad worked. Every weekend they took us to the zoo, to a Greek festival, or something else fun. He carried coolers and strollers. He took John to the bathroom. He changed diapers.

"Walt, can you grab the diaper bag?" Linda asked.

"I already got it, Lin."

We would head over to the soccer field for my soccer games. Linda in her red fox fur coat with a gray leather belt, Montana on the picnic blanket. Walt would go back to the car for the folding chairs. He did whatever Linda asked of him with immediacy, in contrast to how Linda and Dad interacted. Linda and Walt provided us with an example of how a good relationship could function.

After I had played the lead role in, "The Little Red Hen," another parent congratulated him as my father. I set him straight, "He's not my dad." Questions about his place in our family peaked after Erica was born. She had blond hair and blue eyes. By this time he was bald, but he had once been blond. Linda was too, but if someone wanted to gossip, they could have. He stood about as tall as Dad, around six feet. He had once been handsome, but now he'd grown a belly. He had never smoked cigarettes, but he did like cigars. Unlike Dad, though, he drank with Linda. Drinking any amount of alcohol gave Dad a splitting headache.

Walt teased me relentlessly. It drove me crazy.

Once when we went out on the boat, Walt had started the engine up and about three feet from the dock he cut the engine.

"Nicole, I think the engine's broken. We're gonna have to swim for it."

Walt pretended to try to get the engine to start. As I was poised to jump in and swim to the shore for help, he restarted it. I felt relieved until the engine stopped again a bit further from the shore.

"Hell, Linda. I don't know what's wrong."

Again, I stood ready to jump, until he restarted the engine. From my vantage, I couldn't see that he was just turning the key on and off.

"Walt, turn the boat on." He did. Again, I felt relief.

We motored out a bit further and the boat died. I saw the shoreline receding. I often considered whether I could swim to the other shoreline across the peninsula from our house and I thought I could have made it because my swimming was strong. I could save us today.

"Walt, that's enough. You're scaring the kid. Nicole, get back in the boat."

He and Linda were rolling on the floor of the boat laughing.

"Linda, why do you let him do this to me?" I yelled.

"He's just teasing, Nicole," said Linda.

"Well it's mean and I don't like it. Or him," I yelled.

We finally set out on our boat trip. It's a wonder that I ever got into a boat again with Walt or Linda.

Other times, he swatted my butt as I walked by and when I screamed, he chuckled, "Oh, it was a love tap."

"Mom, tell Walt to stop hitting me."

"He's just teasing you."

"But it hurt me."

I think he harassed me to get my attention, but it just made me like him even less than I already did.

Before Linda was on the scene Dad and Walt had owned a gliderport which is an airport for gliders. The first time Walt met Linda, no one would have expected Walt to remain in the picture. They hated each other. Walt felt she was too uppity, and Linda thought Walt was a hick from Kentucky. But not too long later things changed.

Walt had helped Linda plant squash and he lived in a trailer next to Linda and Dad's. Walt took out the trash and mowed the lawn. He made himself indispensable and in that way, they came to work well together. Eventually, the gliderport was gone, but Walt remained.

Walt told stories about me that a father might tell. How I ran around with grapefruits in my shirt saying I wanted to look like Dolly Parton when I was big. He knew all the silly, embarrassing stories.

I hated Walt for his role in our family. I wanted my Dad. I wanted Dad to take an interest in our lives. I wanted him to carry the cooler to the soccer fields and be the consistent presence that Walt was. But neither Dad's job nor his disposition made this possible.

That Friday when Walt arrived at the lake, Linda was ready to start moving into the big house. Saturday more friends came over to help and by Saturday night we were moved in. The outlets weren't covered and other minor things needed fixing, but the house was much larger than the hovel. Linda and Dad's bedroom was downstairs, as was the TV room with the large screen TV and the brown velvet couch.

The house had that freshly painted smell that said to every visitor that it was new. Linda painted my new room a pale pink and Gram made lovely ballooning window shades in white for my room and Erica's room. When I pulled the cord, the fabric puffed out, billowing like clouds. I had a trundle bed, a white desk and chair, and a small portable black-and-white TV. I would spend hours under the covers watching *Moonlighting* in secret on that TV.

I enjoyed watching the adults on *Moonlighting* to see how they interacted with one another, and I knew that Bruce Willis and Cybill Shepherd's character's "liked" each other, even if I wasn't clear what liking meant. Cybil's character reminded me of Linda. They were both beautiful blond women with careers. And I knew Linda loved the show. I don't know if Linda knew I was watching it every week too.

A few nights after moving in Linda said, "Kids, turn out the lights. Let's surprise Dad. He should be home soon."

We ran around turning out the lights. Then everyone stood by the large glass windows that overlooked the driveway.

We giggled as he got out of his truck with his bag and walked to the door of the hovel.

"Mom, aren't you going to say anything to him?" John asked.

"He'll figure it out."

And he did. Dad turned around to see everyone watching him and waved. He walked up the driveway to the new front door, unsurprised. He knew who he had married. Linda wouldn't wait for life to happen. She *made* things happen.

Linda hadn't moved Dad's stuff because his stuff was his responsibility. It also afforded him the option of staying in the hovel. He spent the next few days moving it in. Dad's office in the new house had vaulted twenty-five-foot ceilings with a wall of bookshelves along one side reaching twenty-feet into the air. I helped him put his books in our new library. He had me climb up a ladder and lie on top of the bookshelf to place the books on the highest shelves.

When Linda came in and saw me, she yelled, "Jack, what are you doing?"

"Putting away my books."

"Why is Nicole way up there?"

I had wanted to climb up the ladder and help Dad. I wanted to show him my courage and bravery.

"Nicole, get down," Linda said.

"It's fine," Dad told her.

"No, it's not fine. Get down."

Dad stood on the ladder guiding me down with his hands.

My heart thumped loudly as I realized how dangerously high up I had been. I ran off to play while Linda and Dad fought about the relative intelligence of Dad's idea.

A short distance from Dad's office was the open layout kitchen and dining area in what would have been the front of the boat had the house been a boat. The house had an open concept before everyone wanted such a thing. The living room had white carpet and no furniture. My parents had used Gram's furniture for years and then she had taken it back when we moved to the lake but didn't have space for it in the hovel. In the new house we just didn't have anything to put in there and therefore it remained empty.

Linda's kitchen would have been a dream to many women, but Linda hated cooking and wasn't good at it. She had a few staple recipes: spaghetti, stuffed green peppers (later stricken from the menu because we all hated it), pot roast, tacos, and for a short-time stir-fry. That was pretty much it. She had kept caviar and chutney in her refrigerator before she had married. Once she had us she had a hard time keeping edible food in the fridge. Her new kitchen had new appliances and a small TV for watching cooking shows, ultra-modern at the time.

I loved using the TV to watch the end of *General Hospital* after I got off the bus. Our front door was never locked so I wasn't a latchkey kid. I had no need for a key. Soap operas and MTV were forbidden by Linda, but if she wasn't home, then she didn't know. I wasn't into MTV. After *GH*, *Oprah* came on. I watched that show religiously while I scoured the kitchen, scaling the cabinets looking for something sweet to eat. I would stand at the stove stirring cocoa powder with butter and sugar to make an approximation of a chocolate sauce to eat on ice cream if we had any, or with peanut butter, listening to Oprah talk about losing weight. Some days I would be reduced to toast with cinnamon sugar. But towards the end of *Oprah*, Linda and the kids would come home and I would be done with the TV. I don't know what they had been doing. I never asked.

Later she would call us for dinner and sitting on the table would be meatloaf with a side of fresh-from-the-box mashed potatoes and frozen mixed vegetables, consisting of carrots, peas, and lima beans. We hated these frozen catastrophes of formerly edible substances. Even Linda hated them, but I think she wanted us to have balanced meals, which meant serving these horrible frozen veggies.

We would gobble down the meatloaf with ketchup and mashed potatoes with plenty of butter. But the veggies were pushed around on our plates.

"No one is excused from this table until they've eaten at least one lima bean!" Linda declared, but her heart wasn't in it.

"Mom, I hate lima beans!" I said.

That could go one of two ways. The first way had me sitting at the kitchen table for hours looking at cold limas. The other way was fun.

"I'm a lima!" said Linda.

Slowly, but inexorably Linda rose from her chair, puffed out her chest and put her arms to the side, elbows slightly bent.

"I'm a lima, you're a lima, we're all limas," in a deep voice she chanted over and over.

We ran around the table and fireplace, but we understood that we had to stay in those two rooms. If any of us were caught, then we turned into a lima and had to start chasing the other kids.

The last non-lima won.

"Clear the table kids. It's time for baths."

That night we would leave the limas on our plates uneaten, scraping them into the trash before loading the dishwasher.

Dad thought he had provided well for Linda with the new house. She could be the perfect housewife now. But that's not what Linda wanted. Housewife hadn't ever been her goal. She, consciously or unconsciously, worked out her resentment by refusing to learn how to cook better meals or sending Walt away. These were her small acts of rebellion, her nods to maintaining the unconventional lifestyle she had embraced as a flight attendant. Even if she wasn't flying all over the world, she wasn't going to be normal.

In the basement of the new house sat our living room coffee table, a gigantic wooden utility wire spool, painted brown, on its side, topped with glass. A telephone company worker had given Linda the spool when she had her first apartment in Miami. The projection TV, the focal point of the room, measured six feet wide and was the first of its kind, both technologically and in a private home in the US.

The projection unit sat a few feet in front of the TV and had brown wood paneling around it. While the unit was the size and height of a coffee table, we weren't allowed, under any circumstances, to put anything on top of it. The unit heated up and the fan had to run constantly to keep it cool. To project the shows onto the screen, three large, round, flood-light-looking lights streamed the primary colors onto the screen. If anyone walked in front of the TV, they ruined the picture as they blocked some of the colors and their shadows cast themselves onto the screen.

One day, before we had moved from the hovel into the new house, John and I were playing downstairs, watching TV, and he yanked a toy out of my hand. He was little, not even two yet. I was six. Instead of asking him for it, I grabbed a wire bicycle basket sitting by the large sliding glass windows and threw it at him. John screamed even though I had missed him. Linda came running down the stairs.

"What happened?" she yelled.

We turned to the TV. The screen was made out of what seemed like aluminum foil glued to a slightly concave panel. The basket had two sharp edges and one had caught the TV and created a giant scratch in the upper right-hand corner of the screen.

When Dad saw the scratch and the weapon lying on the carpet, he turned to me and said, "I'm giving you the choice of being grounded for two weeks or a belt spanking. You could've poked John's eye out."

"What does 'being grounded' mean?"

"You have to stay in your room for two weeks, no TV, no fun."

I stood there, only six, contemplating.

"I'll take the grounding," I sobbed.

"Then go to your room. I don't want to see or hear from you," he said.

After choosing the grounding, I sat in my room for five minutes, calming down. I stopped crying. Then I sat there a bit longer and realized there was nothing to do in my room. I thought of the things I would miss out on in the next two weeks. No going to see friends, nor swimming.

Back downstairs I went.

"Can I still get that belt spanking?"

"Are you sure?"

"Yes, Dad. Please. I don't want to be grounded."

He unfurled his belt with the large silver Western belt buckle from his pants and had me bend over his California King bed.

"Nicole, this hurts me more than it hurts you."

Any person hearing this line from a parent screams "bullshit" in their head. I could tell he didn't have his heart in it, though. This was my last belt spanking. He hugged away my tears afterwards.

I stopped crying and was happy with my choice. I felt as if I had paid for my crime. I could move on. I had always preferred taking the Band-Aid off quickly. I hadn't known then, however, that my parents were incapable of enforcing grounding.

We watched the Challenger explode on that big screen TV. We watched *The Muppets* and played life-sized Atari. The scratch remained. It couldn't be repaired or patched. Later on, when we were watching TV and looked for the scratch on it, we couldn't see it. Our brains made up for the scratch and we no longer noticed the imperfection.

1985, Georgia

LINDA often felt lonely out on the lake without any adult conversation. She craved outside stimulation. She had lived in Chicago, Miami, and Atlanta. Her best friends were an expensive phone call away. The locals were too Southern, too provincial, too uncultured to relate to. She was too eccentric for the locals and a Yankee to boot.

Dad tried to make up for Linda's discontent by throwing huge 4th of July parties, inviting everyone they knew. They erected a billboard for the event at the end of our road that read "4th Annual Harkin Pyro Bash!" The parties had a Great Gatsby-like quality with women and men dressed up, walking around with drinks in their hands. I snuck around and listened to the adults.

I caught snippets of conversations, "Did you hear about that pilot in Dallas?" "John Smith is retiring and they're riding their Harleys across the US." "She should have expected things to turn out like that."

Oh, how I desperately wanted to be an adult. Adults were glamorous and allowed to do whatever they wanted, whenever they wanted. Adults were free.

The parties brought my parents together in a way we didn't see often. There was beer, boat rides, and fireworks. Linda and Dad seemed to be a happy couple on those days until the fireworks came out.

Dad had a different sense of safety than Linda and he loved fireworks. The end of the 4th of July party evening was capped off by an expensive fireworks show. Boats came and parked on the lake by our house to watch.

John wanted to help Dad, to please him. Linda hated this but didn't want to start a fight about it in front of her friends. She had learned from Gram, and I had learned from her, the imperative of keeping up appearances. No fighting in public. But this was too much for Linda to watch.

"Jack, he's too young to light fireworks." He was six.

Not long after the sugar cereal and *Aliens* debacles, we were sitting around the large butcher-block dinner table. The conversation with Dad turned to the episode at the grocery store.

"Jack, did Nicole tell you about our trip to the grocery the other day?"

"MOM. Come on."

"She wasn't listening to me and threw a gigantic fit in the store over sugar cereal."

"I just wanted something different to eat," I said.

"Look, if you were willing to throw such a fit with your mother in the store, you love sugar too much," Dad said.

"No. I don't."

"I'll bet you fifty-dollars that you can't go a year without eating sweets," he said.

Only to a fifth-grader in 1986 did fifty-dollars seem like a huge sum for giving up sugar for the year.

"Sure, I can do that," I said.

"OK. We'll see if you can," he said.

Living without sugar took enormous concentration and focus from me. All year long, I told people with pride about the bet, and how I wasn't eating sweets. The specific rule was that I couldn't have any candy, sweets, dessert, refined sugar, or chocolate. If it was something anyone might look forward to eating because it was a treat, then it was *verboten*.

Near my birthday, the halfway point of the year, I planned what to buy with all that money.

"I can get some Barbies and some Barbie clothes, and I can get some Ramona Quimby books, and I can get some new clothes," I told Linda as we drove to dancing.

"I'm not sure you can buy that much stuff with fifty-dollars. I think you could get the books and a Barbie or some new clothes."

I remained silent at this information. I was more than halfway done. I had to decide if keeping the bet was worth it. Because I knew Dad was counting on me, I kept it up. I wanted to show him I could do it.

I didn't sneak any sweets the whole year unless I counted my minor slip-up.

We were having a school party for Valentine's Day. Pink cupcakes and cookies and candies were everywhere. The room was decorated in pink and red. Each kid's desk had a box on top of it made out of a shoebox. On top of the box was a hole for sticking in Valentines. Once the Valentines were passed out, the treats were passed out too.

"No, thank you," I said to the parent handing out cupcakes.

The parent looked at me a little strangely but moved on.

Another parent came by.

"You don't have a cupcake."

She plopped one down on my desk before I could say anything.

On top of this cupcake were three little Valentine hearts. "Be mine" and "Say yes" in pink and green stared up at me.

Everyone in the class knew I wasn't eating sugar because of the bet.

I brushed back my wispy brown hair and then slyly popped one of those little hearts into my mouth when no one else looked.

Immediately I felt sick. I ran to the metal trashcan in the corner of the room and spit out the heart. I told no one.

A few months later, when the time came for me to get paid, my excitement bubbled over. I ran downstairs into Dad's office after he was home from his trip. He sat in his office sorting the mountains of mail he received daily.

"Dad, it's time."

Standing next to him at his desk, I waited for him to look over. On his desk sat a small marble paperweight and piles of important papers.

"Time for what?" he said.

"It's been a year," I said.

"A year since what?"

"Since we made the bet about me not eating any sugar all year."

"What bet?"

I slowly realized he had no clue why I stood there. Dad had forgotten the bet. He had no memory of it. He looked at me with a blank stare and then, as I explained, he was in disbelief. There I was, the eleven-year-old, telling him that he owed me fifty bucks because he had offhandedly made a bet with me a year before. This central part of my year hadn't even made it onto his radar screen, much less impressed him.

As was often the case, I went to Linda.

"Jack, give the kid the money," she said. "Even though you forgot you made the bet, it doesn't mean you don't owe her the money. She didn't eat any sweets the whole year."

He paid up.

room from Erica's side.

Walt, ever present in our lives, hadn't moved with us. Linda lost her best friend and her support. In exchange, she saw Dad more, which turned out to not be such a great thing.

In the old house, when he was calling credit card companies or the phone company to argue about payments for hours on end, we didn't know because his office was so far removed. But in this house, his office sat in what had been the dining room, between the kitchen and the living room. We didn't have much furniture: Dad's credenza, the kitchen table, and Gram's furniture in the living room. Linda had given our couch away to a family in our church whose house had burned down before we moved.

"Where's Dad?" Linda asked one evening.

"He's on the phone."

As Dad walked into the kitchen, Linda said, "Dad, come over here. I need to check your ears."

Confused, he did as told, bending over so Linda could see in his red ear.

"Yep, there's a little telephone growing in his ear. Eventually, it will be big enough that he won't need the actual phone to talk on."

The kids and I giggled. And from then on, when he was on the phone, Linda just said he was growing his little telephone. If he hadn't had his own phone line, his constant phone use would have been even more annoying.

In Georgia, I had loved school because it was my place to get away from my family. Between first and fifth grade, I hadn't missed one day of school. Perfect attendance. I loved reading, but school in Vancouver was a nightmare, every day.

We went to a private Catholic school across the street from our small rented house. Attached to the church, the school had one class for each grade up to eighth. In seventh-grade the students no longer had to wear uniforms but instead could choose what to wear. The children at that small school had been there together their entire lives. I was an outsider, a target for ridicule.

"Why do you talk funny?" asked Monique, the mean girl at school.

"Whaaat due yooou mean?"

"You sound like a hick."

"Eye dooo not."

"Yes, you do."

The three other girls in the class stared at me.

As I became more upset, my accent came out more.

"Eeeyyyyee dooooo noooooot."

The girls laughed at me.

After this, I remained the outcast. What's funny is that in Georgia, I hadn't been southern enough. Yet there in the northwest, I was considered a Southern belle.

Linda and Dad didn't have accents because they were from St. Louis and Boston respectively.

My teacher saw the mean girl and other boys harassing and badgering me day in and day out.

"Are those Keds?"

"Um, yes."

"No, they aren't. Look, the label is falling off," said Monique loudly to the other girls.

I knew they weren't Keds. They were knockoffs.

"You don't need expensive white tennis shoes. They'll just get dirty," Linda had said, not understanding. I tried to glue the blue "Keds" label from my old shoes onto the knockoffs, but I hadn't fooled anyone.

I looked to our teacher, pleading with my eyes, but she looked away. I kept expecting her to do something, and when she didn't, my sense of injustice and unhappiness grew. At this point, I actually thought I wanted to die. I had no friends, I hated my family, and I had difficulty imagining a happier future.

I eventually made two secret friends. Melissa and her mom. She was in my class and lived down the street from me. I spent hours at their house watching *Anne of Green Gables* and *Dirty Dancing*. I played tetherball with her mom in their backyard. But if the other kids in the class had found out, Melissa would have received the same treatment. At school, she watched as they made fun of me. I understood why she kept quiet.

"Look at your arm? Can't you see you're fat?"

I looked at my olive-skinned arm. I didn't see what Monique was talking about.

"You don't have that bone in your wrist that pokes out. Only skinny people have that."

I looked at the mean girl's wrist and the wrists of the other girls in the class. They did, indeed, have that bone sticking out. Mine was missing.

"Can you use your thumb and index finger to wrap around your wrist?" asked the mean girl.

"No, he's not going to get better," replied my gruff and realistic uncle.

But when we arrived in Missoula that day, the nurse had some news.

"His liver numbers are slightly improved. I think you should wait a day to remove life-support. "

"What does that mean?" I asked.

The nurse replied, "Up until now, his body has been slowly dying. Without a functioning liver, he can't get better. We call the measure of liver function his bilirubin number. His body might be healing with these improved liver numbers. Might."

"What's the actual number?" I asked.

"It remains very high. However, it is less than it was yesterday."

"When will we know if he is getting better?" I asked.

"When we know."

At least we didn't have to say goodbye that day.

1988, Washington State to Montana

OUR move to Vancouver was not a good one for Linda or Dad. They were fighting a lot, more than they had before we moved.

One night Linda drove me to dance class in the rain in our new gray mini-van. The lights from the cars were glistening as we drove, and multiplying outward in a long string.

"Now I don't want you to get upset, but your Dad and I are divorcing. You'll have to stay with him."

Staring at the giant wet hill we were driving down, I felt like I was sliding into an abyss. I was old enough to finally sit in the front seat. Linda placed her hand on my arm as we drove, trying to calm me.

"NO, no, no no nooo. You can't. You can't." I reacted explosively, grabbing my arm away from her reach. I screamed at Linda.

"I don't want to be like other kids with divorced parents. I hate you."

"Calm down. I'm trying to talk to you about this."

"How could you do this to me? Or our family?"

"Nicole, it's not that simple. If you don't stay with him, you won't have any money and we won't have any money. I know he won't pay for anything if you're with me."

"I don't want to talk about it."

We pulled into the parking lot. I slammed the car door as I left and Linda never brought it up again.

But what she said lingered in my head. I didn't have any friends to talk about this problem with. I didn't want anyone else to know about it and this fed my sense of despondency and isolation. I worried that even saying out loud that this conversation had taken place might make the divorce actually happen.

A few weeks later Linda and Dad went out together to get our family's Christmas tree. They came back with a tree but less one wedding band. Dad had thrown his out the car window. That had been his second wedding band.

I walked around on eggshells.

Just after I was born, Linda had asked Dad for a divorce. He'd had an affair while Linda was pregnant with me and lost his wedding ring. They had the separation agreement set out, but something happened. Linda didn't leave. The judge had never signed the document.

After Christmas, in January, I turned thirteen. I spent the day becoming certified in First Aid and CPR at a Girl Scout seminar. I expected to have birthday cake, preferably chocolate, a birthday dinner at a Chinese restaurant, and birthday gifts—a new watch please—awaiting me at home.

I went into Linda's tiny master bathroom.

"Mom, I have to show you something in my undies. I can't tell what this is."

Linda took one glance and walked out of the bathroom. She looked up at the popcorned ceiling and said, "Why are you doing this to me today, God?"

No word to me. I hurriedly finished so I could follow her for answers.

"What's wrong? Why won't you talk to me?"

"Not now."

"But I need to know."

"It's your period. Get a pad from under the sink."

In contrast to the blood on Linda's dress years earlier, this looked different. The black gooey substance wasn't what I had expected at all.

"Mom, when are we leaving for dinner?"

"I'm not sure we are."

"What? It's my birthday. We always go out to Chinese food."

We had started this tradition in Georgia where there was only one Chinese restaurant in town and we went once a year.

"I'm not sure we can afford it," said Linda.

Constantly talking about money and whether there was enough had created more low-level anxiety in me. I never quite felt secure in our financial situation, while at the same time I felt like my parents weren't ever telling me the truth. I didn't understand why there wasn't any money. This insecurity scared me as a child.

"But it's my birthday," I pleaded.

"Go talk to your father."

"Dad, we aren't going out to Chinese?" I asked.

"Of course we are, Muppet," Dad replied.

He acted like everything was fine. And, if everything was fine, then

Previously the area had boasted a robust timber industry and a smelter. Both of those were ramping down by then, however. We did have a ski mountain that was known for being socked in with fog, but that kept it from growing too much, which suited the locals just fine.

I settled in quickly to our new home and my new friends.

Gram no longer lived with us, choosing instead to live alone in "Sin City" as her new apartment complex was known in town.

The new house in Montana had the kids' bedrooms and the bathrooms scattered down a long hallway. The house's age was attested to by the wood paneling, orange shag carpeting, and paisley wallpaper. Life was much better in Montana for me even if there was no place to go shopping.

And school was better. The sixteen kids at the rural school I went to were friendly and kind to me. They had also gone to school together since kindergarten, but they were welcoming to outsiders. They knew each other as well as any family. They were considerate of each other's differences. Three of the kids were Jehovah's Witnesses but that didn't stop everyone from bonding.

All year we worked together to make and sell items like school buttons or pencil holders to save for our Montana History Trip. We rode together in an old school yellow bus, traveling a thousand miles together without AC to see all the things we had learned about that year: Custer's Battle Field, Yellowstone National Park, and even Glacier National Park, which wasn't that far from home.

That trip and actually the whole year helped put me back on solid footing. I knew who I was again and more importantly, who I wanted to be.

1988, Montana

"MOTHER, I found a piece of black hair in Jack's luggage," Linda said to Gram. They were talking in the laundry room, around the corner from the hallway to our bedrooms. I stopped in my tracks and sat down on the steps knowing through some sense of Linda's tone that this was a conversation that would stop if either knew I was eavesdropping.

"Maybe it's from the dry cleaners," Gram replied.

"I don't think so," said Linda.

"What are you going to do about it?" asked Gram.

"I don't know."

The subject was changed, but I understood what the hair implied. I just had no idea how to process this information.

"Well, what do you think?" asked my new friend Jenny.

Since we had moved to Montana, Jenny and I had quickly become inseparable.

"Does that mean they'll get divorced? Why would Dad do this?" I asked.

"What are you going to do?" she asked.

"I guess I could ask him," I said.

When Linda and Dad were first married Dad had made some off-hand criticism about the way in which Linda did the laundry and she never did his laundry again. Linda could be that consequential.

After that Dad took his clothes to the dry cleaner so his pants always had a lightly starched crease in them. Like the pillows running down the middle of their bed, this arrangement never struck me as odd.

Why had Linda even been looking in his bags, then? Had she felt generous and was for once cleaning his laundry for him? Or, was she suspicious and looking for proof of her suspicions?

I went downstairs full of bravado. He sat at his credenza reading his mail. The windowless office was in the back basement of the house. The room, rectangular in shape, had large built-in cabinets made out of blond wood at both ends of the room.

"Dad, are you having an affair?"

"Now, Nicole, why would you ask me that?" His voice had a touch of laughter, almost conspiratorial in nature.

"Mom found a black hair in your luggage." He looked up at me. "Are you?" I asked.

"No."

"You're lying."

Dad's face turned red and he jumped up.

"I am not a liar. I have never lied to you. Don't ever call me a liar again if you want to keep living in my house," he yelled.

Yelling was generally Linda's purview. I backed out of the room, but he followed me as I walked away. He had never said anything like this to me before. I ran upstairs crying but I was somehow relieved. He wasn't having an affair. I believed him because of the fervor he had shown.

1988, Montana

FIRST John had wanted a cat and brought one home from a friend's house. There wasn't a chance that a cat could live inside because I was allergic and we had white carpeting throughout our house. So the cat was relegated to the outside. Then we acquired more cats to kill squirrels and mice. Dad's two-car garage had a little door to a cathouse so the cats could go inside when they were cold. The number of cats increased, as is wont to happen with un-spayed and un-neutered animals. The kids played with the cats outside.

We came home one night to find someone had given our fluffy, furry, outside cat, Garfield, a horrible haircut. But who would do such a thing?

I knew right away that Erica had done it, but she denied it. She lied. Her long blond hair and blue eyes often let her get away with things and it drove me batty.

"Who cut the cat's hair?" Linda asked.

We stood lined up on the slate stone in the entryway to our house like the children had done in *The Sound of Music*: from oldest to youngest. We stared at our shoes lined up against the wall. Shoes weren't allowed in the house.

"I'm going to ask each one of you over and over until one of you tells me who did it," Dad promised.

As time went on, Linda and Dad became angrier and angrier. They weren't angry about the cat anymore, they were angry about the lying.

No one fessed up. Linda and Dad relented. Our day moved on. We dispersed.

A bit later I went into Erica's bedroom, all nice-like. I coaxed her down her ladder from her pink loft bed.

"Erica, I know you did it. Just tell me. I promise I won't tell anyone," I said.

"I didn't do it," she replied.

I sat in her room and played with her for a while. Erica basked in the

year?" asked Dad.

"Fifty-two."

"How long do you think you will live?"

"To one hundred," I said.

"OK, you are already sixteen, so take those years as sunk costs. How much time in church would you spend the rest of your life if you go once a week?" he asked.

"Multiply fifty-two times a year times eighty-four years of life left and I have four thousand three hundred and sixty-eight hours. Divide that by twenty-four hours in a day, and I would have one hundred and eighty-two days spent in church. So six months total over my lifetime," I said.

"That's quite an insurance plan. If there is an afterlife, you're getting in for a mere six months of your life. If not, what's six months out of one hundred years?" said Dad.

"But what about you? What do you think happens when you die?" I asked.

"We aren't talking about me," he said.

"What about your body? What happens to it?" I asked.

"You're dead. Your body is dead, so you need to donate your organs. Your body parts that you no longer need can help someone else live," he said. He pulled out his driver's license.

I felt squeamish. I didn't like thinking about my body being dead.

"See, here?" He pointed to the back of the license with the little heart.

"That means I am an organ donor. You should be one too."

So I was.

Dad had grown up in Boston, poor. His father was of Irish descent and his mother had been born into upper class England. Her father, my great-grandfather, was in the British Army and Grammy Harkin grew up in India. She attended a private Catholic school even though her family wasn't Catholic. One day she came home from school and announced she was converting. Her children went to parochial schools, and her two sons were altar boys. She went to church every week and once she was housebound, she watched Mass daily on TV. She always had a Rosary around for praying. Dad's childhood was steeped in Catholicism. And, after thinking about God and religion, he rejected it.

I didn't put much thought into why he hated church. I hadn't put together his having been an altar boy in Boston in the late 60's with his dislike of organized sports and his attendance at Boston College High

School. I am not sure Dad put these things together. Apparently, the whole religion wasn't putting these things together. The topic of child molestation only came up once.

"Dad, why would anyone do that to a child?"

We were driving in his truck listening to the news on the radio.

"I don't know, Nicole. But if anyone did anything like that to any of you kids, I would kill him. I would shoot him dead."

Dad never talked like this. So this stark statement stayed with me.

What I knew to be true at the time was that putting time in at church wasn't enough to get anyone into heaven. Actual belief was necessary, because if I didn't believe, God would know.

But sometimes I wanted to.

One of the problems I had with Christianity was the billions of people who didn't know about Jesus.

Linda and I were standing in her bathroom while she brushed her teeth.

"What happens to the people who don't know about Jesus and the Catholic Church? I mean it doesn't make sense."

She set down her toothbrush and looked me straight in the eyes and said, "Well, they're all going to hell."

I was shocked into silence that she could believe such a thing. Why would God have created these extra people in order to send them all to hell? And why would God only tell some people the "good word?" Especially if we're made in his "likeness." Rationality and faith could not be reconciled. It didn't make sense.

Church, in sum, was the only activity we did together as a family. Otherwise, we were running different directions, living our lives. We ate dinner together a few times a week, but to Linda, church had meaning. It framed her view of the world and gave her an outline for processing the world, even if Dad wasn't with us at church.

Part of growing up is choosing which of your parents' views to embrace and which to let go. Dad's argument rang hollow because he didn't believe it and because after critically considering religion, I didn't believe. To appease Linda I kept up the ruse. I went through confirmation. Uncle Frankie sponsored me. I couldn't shake the sense that there was something out there, some creator, something more to life than dying. Fundamentally, I wanted to believe in something.

1992, Montana

LINDA woke everyone up on school day mornings. The problem with Linda waking everyone up was that she always overslept. Every morning she came racing down the hallway, naked, silk robe on one arm, cigarette in the opposite hand, and flung open the door and yelled like the White Rabbit from *Alice in Wonderland*, "We're late, we're late. Get up!"

It almost seemed like an alarm, because she always said the same thing.

The first night my friend, Jenny, stayed over, she groggily turned to me from the trundle bed and asked, "Did I see what I think I saw?"

"Yes. Ignore her, though. She'll come back."

She always came back, and eventually, everyone went to school.

Our family's time was tightly scheduled before such scheduling was the norm. I always had a job, teaching ski school or waitressing poorly, or I was gone playing soccer or taking dancing classes. Linda spent from 3:15 p.m. until 9 p.m. ferrying her kids all around Montana. And, she hated driving in snow. John did Boy Scouts. Erica took ballet. Montana went to parties where these little guys carted around their desktop computers, hooking them up to play games in a localized network.

There's wasn't much to do in Montana on Friday nights, so generally my friends and I would hang out at each other's houses. If it was Saturday then we were waiting for Saturday Night Live to come on. We didn't care if it wasn't live because of the time difference. One night I had hung out at a friend's home and while driving home my car died. Fortunately, I was in front of a different friend's house. Unfortunately, that friend was in Austria on an exchange. I had no choice but to knock on her parents' door. I needed help.

"Well, hey, Nicole. What are you doing here?" said her mom, Ralene.

Ralene and Linda should have been friends—they were cut from similar cloth, outsiders who moved to Montana because of their families, not out of some love for the state.

"My car died. Can I call my mom?"

"Sure," she replied.

"She'll come and get me," I said.

"Linda, the car died. Can you pick me up? I'm at Laura's house," I said.

"No," she replied.

"But Mom. What? No?" I said.

"You'll have to figure this out on your own," she said.

"What do you mean? I need you to come and get me," I said with much more urgency.

"Nicole, figure it out."

As I hung up the phone, I started crying a little bit. Ralene asked, "What's wrong?"

"My mom won't come and pick me up," I said.

I worried about what Ralene would think of me and my family and I was embarrassed that my mom left me stranded.

Ralene said nothing and kindly took me home. I called the emergency roadside assistance in the morning.

Linda had pissed me off. She'd made me look stupid in front of my friend's mom.

After finishing her chauffeur duties every day, Linda drank. And most nights she didn't drink to excess, only three or four glasses of wine.

I sometimes caught her at the wrong time.

Trotting down the stairs to her sewing area, I said, "Linda," before I reached the last step.

"I forgot I need money for lunch out. We're going off campus."

"I don't have any money, Nicole."

She picked up her cigarette from the crystal ashtray.

"But Mom, I need the money." I worried about what my friends would think if I couldn't go out to lunch.

"Get a job then," she yelled.

She was a mean drunk, but she didn't get drunk often. Dad called it snake juice. This time things devolved.

"You always say you don't have any money," I screamed back.

"That's because I don't."

She kept working on the outfit she was sewing for a Barbie. A mini fur stole from black sheep's wool.

I kept pushing. "Come on. I need the money."

"Like I said, get a job, Nicole."

I had a job. I always had a job, just for this reason. I had my own money, but I didn't like to use my money to pay for food. That was my parents' responsibility. I used my money to pay for things like Birkenstocks. Linda hated them, but they were part of my social group's uniform.

I walked away. I wasn't making any headway with her. If I asked her again in the morning, she might relent. Or, I could check her wallet—see if she *was* broke. And, if all else failed, I could raid her change jar, a gigantic glass stein in her dressing room. The change just sat there for the taking. Did she know I did this? We each took money from it. She must have realized.

Linda hadn't come to pick me up that night my car broke down because she had been drinking. She might even have been done drinking for the night. Red wine in a box was her favorite because no one could tell how much she drank and it was cheap. In the morning a wine glass might be found downstairs sitting on the half wall in her sewing area, inevitably with red lipstick around the rim.

Her drinking was never a topic of conversation. No one ever said, "Your mom's an alcoholic." I knew what an alcoholic was. I knew parents who were. I knew kids whose parents had frozen to death in front of their homes because they had come home drunk and passed out in winter before going inside. But when my car had broken down, I hadn't connected Linda's glasses of wine with her behavior.

John often hid her cigarette cartons in the woods. He sometimes hid the wine too. So the clue phone had rung for him, at least.

She overslept every day because she drank too much every night. She was a functional alcoholic. I was so self-absorbed that I couldn't or wouldn't see it.

1992, Montana

LINDA liked to chat with people. She constantly struck up conversations with people, especially while waiting in line. Before cell phones there was Linda to pass the time.

She chatted with a friend's mom as we waited to check out at the grocery. Somehow the conversation turned to my resemblance to Linda, or lack thereof.

"Oh, well Nicole's adopted."

"Mom, tell the truth. I'm not adopted."

With a hand in front of her mouth, she replied to the other mother, "She's a little sensitive about it."

My friend's mom was confused at this point. She didn't understand what was happening. She thought I was adopted.

"Mom, stop it!"

"That's why we don't look alike," she went on.

"Mom, come on, tell her the truth."

Linda shrugged her shoulders towards the other woman as if to say, "What can I do?"

Just like The Wicked Witch, Linda wouldn't know where to stop.

"Why do you have to do that, Linda? It's so embarrassing."

"Oh, it was just a joke."

Not too long after this Linda sent Dad to a meeting at school. Picture a high school classroom filled with anxious teenagers and anxious parents listening to a teacher go on and on about a trip to Germany over the upcoming Christmas holiday. The room had German posters around and standard-issue desks and chairs in rows for the students by day and smelled faintly of antiseptic cleaner. The meeting wasn't the most interesting meeting but to me it seemed important. Everyone brought their families. This trip to Germany was huge for most families. Sending your child around the world was a big deal, but not to mine. Our teacher began discussing the trip, taking questions, going through the itinerary.

And then Dad got up and walked out.

Maybe he went to the bathroom, I thought. But after waiting ten minutes for his return I went to find him.

He sat on the linoleum floor outside the room reading.

"Dad, what are you doing?"

"Reading my book. What does it look like I'm doing?"

He had a thick hardback Robert Ludlum-type book. He always bought the hardbacks because he donated the books after reading them and then wrote off the full value of the book from his taxes.

I had thought it was strange when he brought the book to the meeting.

"Why?" I asked him in the hallway.

"The meeting's boring."

He had a point, but the meeting was mandatory and it was important that Dad behave because I took German to be in class with my high school crush—Brent—who was in the meeting with his dad.

I am certain many other parents wanted to leave, but didn't.

"Let me know when the meeting's over."

No one else noticed or at least no one else said anything about my Dad just leaving the meeting.

A few weeks later I was back in the same classroom, this time with Linda. I couldn't allow Dad to go to the meeting again. The teacher, balding with a belly, asked if there were any final travel tips anyone wanted to share before the trip. Linda raised her hand.

She had been a flight attendant and Dad was a pilot. My family, and by proxy, me, were part of the travel industry. Thus, I expected Linda's travel tip to be excellent.

"Linda, what's your tip?" the teacher asked.

"When our family goes on vacation, we take our old, ratty, stained underwear and wear them one last time. Then we throw them away at the hotel so we have more room to bring back souvenirs."

I considered crawling under my desk and thought to myself, "Maybe I *am* adopted. We don't even look alike. How could she do this to me? Why can't she be like other parents?"

In third grade, I had yelled at Linda, "You didn't pack my bags the right way." She never packed my bags for me again. So, I didn't even know that my family did this with their old undies. I certainly didn't do it.

1994, Indiana

AT the end of high school the only thing I wanted was to leave Montana. I wanted out. I didn't think I needed to be close to my family. I wanted to live in a city and have an important job making my own money. I wanted independence.

I only applied to one college, Purdue. In high school an English teacher had us identify schools that were good fits for our interests. I wanted to study paleontology, German, Political Science, and Aeronautical Engineering or so I thought. Purdue and Montana State University came up as the two schools in the US that had these various majors. I had heard of Purdue. I knew it was a big school and, most importantly, it wasn't in Montana. Luckily, I got in. Dad had always promised to pay for the college where I was admitted.

My freshman college roommate was from Grosse Pointe, Michigan, a rich suburb outside of Detroit. She chewed tobacco in her lofted bed and didn't like me, which made me dislike her. She reminded me of the mean girl from seventh grade in Vancouver.

Forty thousand students attended Purdue which made making friends hard. I couldn't find my group of people, and I still had my high school boyfriend, which left me pining for home. I wanted to be someplace where people wanted me around, and because I didn't have a close friend group, college wasn't that place. I missed my family more than I expected to. Adding to this malaise, I still didn't know what I wanted to be when I grew up. The options overwhelmed me.

I thought sororities were interesting. To join one meant an application and then interviews with each of the houses—called "rush"—followed by some opaque process by which you were matched with a house. This was how I found myself sitting in the basement of a sorority during rush. On the couch next to me was a tall redhead. We'd been allowed into the basement to warm up because outside it was below freezing.

"Where are you from?" asked the redhead.

77

"Montana."

"Oh, do you have to wear coats there?"

She thought Montana and California were close to one another. They were closer to each other than to Indiana, where we were, but the states couldn't be much more different. After I explained, she laughed. Finally, a friend.

Sorority rush offered me a lifeline: a group of like-minded women with whom to spend my hours, women to explain how to navigate the system. Friends.

At the beginning of my sophomore year of college, Linda, Erica, Montana, and I drove back to school towing my yellow Geo Metro convertible. I moved into my sorority house with its large white columns. We shared rooms, but all slept in one large cold dorm, on the third floor of the house. In a throwback to earlier times, men were not allowed upstairs into our rooms or, heaven forbid, the sleeping dorm.

Later that year, I wanted a bigger car to fit more of my sorority sisters in, and, with a bigger car, I could move my stuff more easily. I didn't really need it, however.

"Dad, I need a bigger car here. They have ice storms. It's dangerous to drive the Metro."

"Fine. I'll talk to Mom about it."

That had been easier than I had expected.

At the time, I didn't understand what "needing" something meant. Dad told me to only use the credit card he gave me for real emergencies. Wasn't a new bra a need? My other bra had broken. Dad had yelled at me when he got the bill. I hadn't yet formulated a way of discerning the difference between a want and a need. I hadn't needed to.

A few weeks later Dad drove out from Montana with the Suburban. I was excited because he had never seen my college.

Most of my girlfriends' parents came once a month to see them. They took their daughters out to Wal-mart and to dinner. They bought food and other supplies for their kids. That is what I wanted, a normal parent visit.

Why didn't my parents want to come see my school or visit me? They lived far away, and even if the plane ticket was free, the rest of the trip wasn't. And, I had chosen to go to Indiana for college, far from home. I had wanted to leave Montana and my parents never tried to persuade me otherwise. Their not coming to see me resulted from my choice to leave.

Before cell phones, the sorority had one phone line and we took turns sitting by that phone throughout the day and night, taking messages for our sisters as people called. We could look out the windows to the front door of our house, watching who came and went. The sorority system was at a kind of tipping point with respect to the institution: women no longer felt they needed the supervision of a house mother and parents were more comfortable sending their daughters to college, unsupervised. The system was becoming vestigial.

I sat in the phone lounge waiting for Dad to drive up.

"Hey, Muppet. Here are the keys to the Suburban. Where's the Metro?"

"Parked there. Do you want to see the house?"

I handed him the keys.

"I need to get on the road. Let me put my suitcase into the Metro and I'll be on my way."

"WHAT?"

"I've got to get back on the road."

"I wanted to show you my school and go out to dinner and go shopping. You can't just leave. I want you to see my room and meet some of my friends."

"Let's drive around campus," he relented.

I showed him where I studied and the stadium. I showed him where I had lived when I was a freshman. He seemed harried and rushed.

Then we drove across town in separate cars. He took me to Chinese for dinner. Then he said he had to get on the road. I watched him drive away and was sad, but I didn't know what else to do. He wasn't interested in learning about my life or where I lived. But he had brought me the car, driving it across the country. These two contradictions confused me. Only years later would I understand. At least I had the Suburban.

1995, Montana

TIME trundled on and when I came home for Christmas during my third year of college things seemed unchanged.

As I walked down the small set of stairs by the laundry room on my way to the kitchen, I came upon my parents hugging, kissing, and laughing, something they never did. I had sat on these same steps years earlier listening to Linda tell Gram she thought Dad was having an affair.

Linda and Dad were talking about Dad retiring and how they would drive a Gold Wing motorcycle throughout the US, never mind that Linda hated motorcycles and had three children at home.

"What color will we get?" asked Linda.

"Blue."

"I don't want to sit behind you."

"We'll get the sidecar."

They had even gone to the dealership to scope out the motorcycles.

"Why don't you two cut the act and stop pretending to like each other?"

Linda and Dad looked at me in shock and disbanded. Linda went into the laundry room and Dad into the kitchen.

I don't know why I said it. My anger at their feigned happiness—where did it come from? Their living unhappily with each other was normal, but for them to pretend to live happily with each other offended me. People don't treat one another the way they did if they were happy and loved each other. Ah, but people can both love and hate at the same time. I didn't know this at the time.

Christmases in our house were momentous affairs. Linda and Dad could do Christmas. They knew how to cooperate on this yearly event. Dad had gone so far as to raise the roof on the house so we could have an even bigger Christmas tree: twenty-four feet tall.

In order to handle a tree of that size, we had to take the tree to the carwash by trailer and wash it before it came in the house. A tree that old was dirty. We let it dry in Linda's garage overnight. Once the tree had dried we sawed it in half. Next, we attached the top half of the tree to the rope and pulley system that hung from the wooden beam in our living room for just this reason. Once hoisted up, the bottom half of the tree had to be positioned under the dangling top half of the tree. Inevitably we would forget to put the angel on the top half of the tree before pulley-ing it up, so we needed to lower the top half down again once we realized it was missing.

The gifts on Christmas morning were arranged on two white sheets doubling as Christmas tree skirts. Gram had an amazing method of tying bows out of satin ribbon. She looped the ribbon over and over on her hand and folded the loops in half and cut little "V" shaped wedges out of the middle of the loops before tying a knot there. Then she pulled the ribbon loops out, alternating sides until half of the bow was complete. The other side had the same treatment. The presents were wrapped with these large bows. A large model train set used at Christmas went around the tree as well. The end effect was like waking up in a fairytale land where everything looked perfect on the outside and the kids received every wish on their Christmas list.

Gram had begun the tradition of massive Christmases. She spent months baking cookies when Linda was little and storing them in large white boxes in a specific cookie cupboard. She gifted these to friends and neighbors during the holidays. The Christmases of my childhood were much less extensive than Linda's were. Gram had been compensating for her sad childhood Christmases in a children's home.

Christmas that year was wonderful. We trimmed the gigantic tree together. Two hundred six-inch-tall gingerbread men that Gram had baked and intricately decorated as Santas and elves hung on the tree and the tree seemed to infuse the cookies with a special taste. The icing hardened and complimented the ginger taste of the cookies. As the weeks before Christmas went on, we ate every cookie off the tree.

From our house, it took about an hour to drive up the mountain. Our family went skiing every weekend during winter. Normally Linda was forced to drive up and down the winding mountain, but if Dad was home, he took us. Before I left for college, Jenny had almost always come with us. The kids took ski lessons and she took lessons from Dad. I worked as a ski instructor. The pay was excellent and I received a free skiing pass. Dad would have bought my ski pass, but I wanted the money. My search for independence meant that I missed out on the chance to spend this time skiing with Dad. I had this sense that my parents were static. They would always be there.

That Christmas, the kids needed downhill ski racing outfits, and Linda and Dad both thought that the ones off the rack were too expensive. Santa had brought Linda state-of-the-art computerized sewing and serging machines. Linda spent most of her time in the evening crafting, as she called it. Downstairs in our finished basement, she had an area with her sewing notions, sewing machine, and serger. The space was six-feet by twelve-feet and enclosed by a half wall. Along the walls, were the same blond cabinets that lined Dad's office on the other side of the wall.

Inside these cabinets were all manner of items: yarn, material, buttons—lots of buttons, she collected them—scissors, baskets, ribbon, thread, paper, markers, cardboard, old note cards. She collected the stuff from the thrift stores she frequented. The copious amounts of these supplies gave me a sense of possibility when I looked at it. There were so many projects she could dream up with these materials. Linda lined baskets, made pins in the shapes of whimsical doodles she had drawn, and sewed Barbie clothes. She didn't sew clothes for people. Ever. She didn't find it interesting or cost effective. She sold the stuff she made for a few years at the Ivy Cottage, a co-op she and Gram started downtown. Sometimes she sent me handmade greeting cards with funny cartoons or flowery motifs to sell at school. I never even tried to sell these things. I kept them in my closet in boxes. At least two of the cabinets in the basement had her built up stock of items she had made which was waiting to be sold or used.

She and Dad spent a few weeks sewing together after Christmas in the basement. The fancy sewing machine and serger could be programmed or attached to computers to enact even more complicated patterns. Together they had cost thousands of dollars. Linda's old Singer moved into a cabinet after the arrival of the new machines. Dad had bought the neoprene material and the patterns on a trip to Portland and he and Linda proceeded to sew the racing suits for John, Erica, and Montana. The suits were difficult to sew because of the neoprene's thickness, and the kid's suits needed to be as tight as possible to make them more aerodynamic while they skied. Linda and Dad both hunched over the sewing table, Dad sitting running the sewing machine and Linda holding the material as it was fed through the machine. When they had a combined project, they could act as a team.

We—my siblings and me—were their combined project. We turned out like the ski racing outfits: well-made, but with some imperfections.

Dad had some inner calculus that we weren't privy to regarding money. He bought ski passes but balked at giving Linda more money for food. He bought new cars but didn't want to pay for gas. Our gigantic house was always cold in winter because he didn't want to pay for heat. In contrast, in the summer it was always freezing, because the AC ran all the time, even though it didn't get that hot in Montana. He wanted the kids to ski race but didn't want to pay for racing suits.

John and Montana loved ski racing, but Erica hated it. It petrified her. When Linda and Dad were first married, Linda had skied too. Dad had taken her down a slope that was too difficult and she stopped skiing. She had wanted to participate in these activities Dad was interested in and she had tried, but he had scared her, so she just stopped.

To become a ski instructor years earlier I had to demonstrate that I could teach someone how to ski.

"Linda, can I teach you how to ski?"

"Well, I don't know."

"Come on, Mom. It won't be bad."

She hedged a bit more.

"It'll be fun. I'm a good teacher."

She wore my old pink ski outfit with fluorescent green and yellow stripes, and she looked great.

Hour after hour, I showed her how to make a pizza slice with her skis. She fell and got up. We made more pizza. She used the rope pull to go up and down the bunny slope. Other people in my class brought kids. She was the only adult.

"When's lunch?" Linda asked.

"Um, can we do one more run?"

"I need a break."

What she needed was a cigarette. After lunch, she didn't move. I could tell she was done for the day. Lessons over. She had been a real sport but she never skied again. She loved the film "Troop Beverly Hills" with Shelley Long, and she tried to be that adventurous. She wanted to show us we could do anything we wanted to do. Anyone who didn't know her well would have thought she was fearless. But Linda was afraid of skiing, afraid of driving on snowy roads, and afraid as she watched her children careen down the mountain every weekend.

Why did she do these things she was afraid of? Dad wasn't there most of the time. But she still did what he, and we, wanted her to do to the largest extent of her abilities. We loved skiing because Dad loved skiing. Even though he wasn't present, we were there together on the hill trying to garner his approval.

Linda wanted us to have a stable childhood with a broad range of experiences. Her childhood had been the opposite of stable. Her father had died in WWII. At age nineteen, Gram was left with a baby, no husband, and no education. But Gram knew how to work hard, as a child of The Depression, and then she met my step-grandfather. They got married in short order, and she had two more children.

I never had a grandfather. Dad's father had died when I was a baby and when I asked Gram about her husband, she had always changed the subject.

When I was six-years-old, Gram had moved to Houston, Texas, with her boyfriend and I visited them for the summer. We went to the pool often and we worked in her garden. We took trips in their motor home and went to Six Flags. We had a grand time together. She showed me pictures of Linda and her siblings when they were small. Stamped on the back of the photos was the word "reviewed."

"Gram, what does it mean, 'reviewed'?"

"Nothing."

"But Gram, who stamped it?"

"No one."

"Why?"

"That's enough, Nicole."

I knew by the tone of her voice that was the end of this conversation.

Linda's childhood wasn't turbulent merely because of her biological father dying, but because her stepfather had embezzled a substantial amount of money from the State of Illinois and ended up in prison for five years. The photos had been sent to him there and stamped reviewed before they were given to him.

By the time I was born, Linda's stepfather was out of the picture.

That life and Linda's relationship with her father were far behind her when she and Dad were sewing in the basement. She had four kids and lived in Montana. She did, however, keep her nails painted red.

1996, Montana

OUR favorite nurse asked to talk to Linda outside of the room.

"Linda when you guys aren't here an Asian woman visits Jack. She's very nice and puts Asian oils and herbs on him. I thought you would want to know."

I could hear this conversation from inside the room.

"Who's that woman?" I asked afterward.

"Your father's girlfriend," Linda said.

"How long have you known about her?"

"Nicole, you asked your father about her years ago."

"But Dad said he didn't have a girlfriend."

"He lied."

"The girlfriend is coming here," Linda said to Walt, who had flown in to help Linda. I had never seen this girlfriend while I visited him.

"Well, tell the hospital to only let people in to see Jack who you allow," said Walt.

That's what Linda did.

I watched Linda as my brain churned. The girlfriend explained a lot of things. Why Linda was always mad at Dad. Why Dad sat "on reserve" in Portland a lot waiting for other pilots to call in sick. Sometimes he had to go to work when someone else called in sick. But most of the time he could go about his life. If your family lives in the same town as you are based, this works great. If your family lives in Montana and you are based in Portland, you might bid to work reserve if you wanted to spend more time with people living in Portland.

The previous year, before I had gone home for the summer, Linda had called me. I was staying with a college friend for a few days.

"Nicole, Dad wants to take you, Erica, and Montana to Korea on one of his trips. Do you want to go?" Linda asked.

"Yes. That's awesome. Why not John too?"

"He's working."

John had begun working at a local auto body shop, at first to fix his car, which he had crashed, and then to make money.

I flew to Portland that day and met Dad and the kids. Dad had my passport. My parents never did this kind of thing.

On the plane, Montana wanted to play his Nintendo Game Boy. I told him it wasn't allowed. Dad walked back to business class to check on us.

It felt so cool to have my Dad fly us to Asia. I was proud of him.

"Dad, Nicole says I can't play my Nintendo. Can I?"

"Of course."

"But Dad, the rules say he can't."

"I'm the pilot, Nicole. I set the rules."

His rebuke hurt my ego.

In Seoul, we went shopping at the markets. The hotel room was miniature. We were there for thirty-six jet-lagged hours. I didn't eat much because everything smelled or looked strange. Dad finally took us to an American style diner where we had eggs and toast, which also tasted odd.

One of the flight attendants, an Asian woman, was with us the whole trip. I felt annoyed because I wanted my Dad to myself. Dad had introduced her as a friend.

As I sat in the hospital I put the pieces together. Dad had taken his girlfriend on this trip with us. Had Linda known this? No way.

I thought back to the trip and the smells and the craziness of taking his kids on a trip to Seoul. We had landed and gone shopping in the gigantic markets looking for jumpsuits for Linda and silk shirts for Gram.

"I'll take ten shirts," Dad said.

The vendor knew Dad. But when Dad took out a checkbook, I was shocked.

"What are you doing? You can't pay with a check Dad," I said.

Paying with a check in a Korean market seemed like the dumbest thing ever, but the vendor did indeed take the check.

"Nicole, shut up."

I wonder if Dad thought that by introducing us to his girlfriend he could test the waters and see how we responded to her. None of us took to her then.

As I remembered this trip, and the woman, I wondered if the herbs and oils his girlfriend put on him helped him. Maybe they made a difference.

Maybe she had saved him.

Before we had moved west, every year before Christmas, Dad took me to downtown Atlanta to Neiman Marcus. We drove his big blue Chevy truck and went straight to the lingerie. I knew Neiman's was Linda's favorite store and Dad knew Linda's sizes off the top of his head. He told the sales associate the sizes and she'd collect a bunch of bras and panties for us to look at. He picked two and I picked one, and the salesgirl wrapped them up. Then, at the last minute, he asked the salesgirl to wrap another set separately in a different size.

On Christmas day, I said, "Linda, I thought Dad had more packages for you?"

"That's all, Muppet," said Dad.

"It is? I know we got her a set that was red? Where did those go?" I said.

The room became silent as everyone, Linda, the kids, Walt, and Gram, turned to see what Dad would say.

John broke the silence, talking about his Transformers. The moment was passed over by most of the room as a kind of glitch—an error—to be ignored.

Now, in Montana, Linda was mad at Dad, so she stayed home in Kalispell. She didn't want him dead, but she didn't want to be at the hospital with him either. Or maybe she did want him to die. I can't say for certain. She loved him, a lot, but she faced a future of taking care of four children and a disabled husband. Staying home was a way for her to process the situation without being in the middle of the situation. She could tally up the glitches to see clearly what had been hinted at for years.

1996, Montana

I worked at the fuel station south of town Monday through Thursday from 6 a.m. to 2 p.m. so I could go see Dad the rest of the time. I had worked before as a camp counselor, a cook, a waitress, a ski school instructor, and a telemarketer. None of these jobs had mattered in the same way. I hadn't needed the jobs to pay for my life.

In the cold Montana winters, the temperature was often some minus number, and it was pitch black when I arrived at work. I opened the doors, then grabbed the clipboard and headed out to the pumps. Each pump had a kind of odometer on it and I recorded that number before turning them on. On full moon nights, I could see my shadow as I raced around to the pumps. I didn't spend much time outside of my car in winter.

After reading the pumps it was time to open up. I put the coffee on and then chopped up the fruit. The management was experimenting with selling chopped melons and people liked the fruit. They liked buying fruit from a fuel station. But before cutting the melons, I had to get the real food ready, the popcorn and hot dogs. I threw a few sausages on the perpetually rolling warmer, too, just in case. Finally, I opened my till.

"Hi. How are ya doing today?" I asked.

"Good. Pack of Marlboros please."

I sold a lot of cigarettes. I felt somehow complicit in these people's demise.

"Hi. How are you doing?"

"Could I get five dollars on pump three?"

Nobody cared how I was—nobody asked. If someone had asked, I would have told them I was bored and sad and scared. My dad was almost dead, he had a girlfriend, we were about to lose our house, and I was working at a fuel station.

"How's your day going?"

"Hot dog to go. Onions."

All. Day. Long.

Looking in my till one day I saw something strange, different. It was a Mercury dime with a Roman God stamped on it. That became my definition of a good day, finding ten cents.

One of the hardest parts of a job like that was the inability to go to the bathroom before your co-workers arrived. I worked the whole time. Standing. Stocking. Answering the phone. Alone much of the time.

My boss was a short woman who had worked there for fifteen years. She looked like a mom and was smart, smarter than her job. I thought she could have done more with her life, but what did I know of her life?

My boss liked me and she hated me. She saw me as a privileged kid who didn't need the job. What did she know about me? She was half right. I needed the job. However, I did my job with an attitude of someone who wasn't supposed to be working in a fuel station.

"Nicole, could you get the mop and clean the bathroom?"

"I thought Mike usually did that?"

The bathroom at the fuel station was abysmal, no matter how often it was cleaned.

"I need you to clean it. Mike's busy," my boss replied.

"I need to restock the candy. Can it wait?"

By wait, I meant wait for Mike to do it.

"No, it's your job. Look, Nicole, you'll leave this job one day and never look back. You can show as much disdain for this job as you want, but this is our life. This is where we work. We aren't leaving, so making us feel bad about staying here is mean."

Of course she was right. I cleaned the bathroom.

1996, Montana

MONTANA is home to one of the few triple divides in the world. If rain falls on Triple Divide Peak, a mountain in Glacier National Park, the water has the opportunity to flow in three directions: to the Atlantic, the Pacific, or the Arctic. I always wondered how the direction the water would go in was determined. If it falls directly on the tippy top, which way would it flow? Would it split into three drops, each going in a different direction? Or, would the angle of the next drop, falling on the first drop decide? Did the pressure from this next drop determine where the water would flow?

We wanted Dad to live so the pressure of waiting for him to die would end. The pressure lay on top of us—almost suffocating us. Every time the phone rang, I expected someone to tell me that he was dead. Every improvement was met with a setback. No doctor was willing to tell us he would make it, but they were quick to give us the worst-case scenario.

"If he does live, he won't have any quality of life."

We were there on the top of the triple divide for quite some time. In one direction, lay Dad dead. In a second direction he improved, and life went back to normal. In the third direction, Dad survived, but things changed nonetheless. We contemplated the first two options, not even understanding that a third way existed.

The feeling of absolute knowledge is the same between religious zealots and doctors: they believe they know the answers to life's most vexing questions, but they don't—not really. No one can know, even with medicine's most advanced techniques or with the prayers of the most faithful. No one knows who will live and who will die.

Even as I hated this absolutism, I asked the doctors over and over, like the oracles of history, to tell me, to give me some sign that he would live.

Dad's improvement happened slowly from that day the nurse told us his liver numbers had improved. Each day he improved a bit more. And the next day and the next. He awoke and moved from ICU to the step-down ICU.

Then he moved to a regular hospital room. His muscles had atrophied and he needed to relearn how to do everything: brush his teeth, put on his shirt and pants, tie his shoe laces, feed himself, cut his food, hold a coffee mug to drink his coffee, sit up in bed, turn himself to the edge of the bed, stand up, hold a book, move a mouse, put on his watch, take off his clothes to shower, wash his hair, dry himself off, walk. Neither driving a car nor flying a plane were mentioned.

He hadn't died. He wasn't a vegetable, but he was like an infant who could talk.

We knew when we knew. But the reality of what was happening didn't clobber us over the head in the same way his initial illness had. His improvements were gradual, as was our understanding that he wasn't the same person.

The process gained momentum steadily as a different drug, bandage, or medical device was removed. But he was still on a fair amount of pain medicine. He watched The Weather Channel constantly in his hospital room.

"Montana, move the fan, please. It's going to melt," said Dad from his hospital bed.

"What are you talking about, Dad?" asked ten-year-old, but almost six-feet-tall, Montana.

"Montana, the fan. Move it away from the window."

"But it can bring in the cool air. Aren't you hot?"

"Montana, the fan's made out of chocolate. You can see that. If it stays in the sun, it will melt."

We looked at the fan and then at Dad. Everything and nothing had changed.

His healing process took months. Once he was awake, he could make his own medical decisions. Linda wasn't going to visit him often. His girlfriend couldn't be kept from him. I never saw her, but I knew she visited sometimes. The room would have the scent of incense or medicinal herbs.

We walked a delicate balance in our conversations, at some points being radically honest while I had to clip his toenails or help him go to the bathroom, seeing him partially naked. But we didn't discuss the girlfriend. Discussion would have made his girlfriend real. I wasn't ready to confront that.

I was mad at him about the girlfriend and about lying to me but he had almost died, could still easily die. I didn't want our relationship to be strained. Once everything was back to normal then we could confront this.

I went to Missoula as often as I could, but helping him wasn't easy.

"Muppet, can you scratch my back?"

"Sure, where?"

"First you have to pull me forward. Can you put some lotion on my back?"

"I know. Yes, give me a second."

"Do I have any water?"

"Here you go."

"No ice?"

"I'll get some."

"How about some apple juice?"

"Can you have apple juice?"

"Nicole, get me the damn juice."

Dad couldn't see our plight. He couldn't see how almost losing him had affected us. His trauma was his alone—which was normal if difficult to handle.

"Dad, you're acting like a jerk. I'm going shopping, and I hope that when I get back you'll have adjusted your attitude. I don't have to be here."

And that's what I did. I walked downtown to the one department store with the sun on my back that sunny spring day in Missoula. This being Montana, there were a number of bars too. I bought some black Lancôme eyeshadow, in no way appropriate for wearing in Montana, and fish-shaped earrings. I felt guilty for leaving him there, but I felt good that I asserted myself and let Dad know he couldn't walk all over me. Or maybe I merely asserted myself to myself. I didn't have to allow Dad to manipulate me. I was an adult. I was there of my own free will.

The strange part of sitting by someone's bedside who is in a coma is that when they wake up, they don't remember you were there the whole time they were in the coma. He didn't remember how long I had held his limp hand, how often I ran out to the nurses' station to help him, or how I had cared for him. He was asleep and then he was awake.

I was there for him because I loved him. The fact that he didn't appreciate my love and efforts hurt my feelings.

Months earlier and a few days after the trip to Missoula where we were to say our final goodbyes to Dad, Linda and I had stood in her bathroom. It was decorated in browns and tans, showing signs of age but still nice. When I wanted to chat with her loitering in the bathroom was a good place to do so. She was brushing her teeth. She compulsively brushed because she was worried her teeth would fall out, and she was trying to keep the cigarette and coffee stains off of them. After brushing, she lit a cigarette. She was allowed to smoke in her bathroom, in the kitchen, and in her sewing area in the basement. These were my little brother's rules.

"Mom, why are you still smoking?" I asked, worried that she might die too.

"Not now."

"You know it's bad for you. What if you die too? Then where would we be?"

"After we get through this crisis, I promise I will quit. We have to get through this, though. I can't handle stopping right now."

I believed her. I thought that after Dad recovered, she would quit smoking. I think she believed it too. We believed that if Dad recovered, we would change our lives and become our better selves. We needed to get through this crisis and everything would be OK.

Sometimes at night, I slept in Linda's room with her. In front of their bed was a large screen TV before these things were ubiquitous. We took turns sleeping in her bed. Montana did it the most—he was still little then. Her bed was big and cozy with a fluffy down comforter.

Lying there under the bedspread and blankets I could hear her breathing. Although she slept propped up, she coughed throughout the night, but I was used to the noise. It was comforting. I knew she was still there.

My family operated like six little planets occasionally intersecting and interacting with one another. None of us took into consideration how our individual actions affected the others. However, while Dad withered away near death in the hospital, we had pulled it together as a family. The fighting had stopped. We worked to get through it together. I worked at the fuel station, Erica worked at the movie theater, and John had the job at the body shop repairing cars. Walt went back to work as a machinist even though he had recently retired. Gram bought groceries. We had this sense that Dad would wake up and tell us where his money was and then everyone would be paid back and life would just keep going on that same track.

Linda told her close friends about the lack of money and we lived in a small town so once a few people knew, everyone knew. The community helped us, too. A neighbor had paid to fill our heating oil tank when it ran out in February.

This crisis stripped everything to its absolute essence. We were a family trying to survive a crisis of physical, financial, and emotional proportions. Figuring this out became our priority—all without Dad in the picture.

Later, Dad moved from the hospital in Missoula to a rehab center in Kalispell. He rode in an ambulance the one hundred and twenty miles back. He returned to where he began.

The rehab center was on the other side of the local hospital in a new wing. Dad reluctantly shared a room with another patient. They tried to pair patients with similar maladies in rooms. There was a debate as to whether Dad should be put with another stroke victim, a heart operation patient, or with an infectious disease patient. Dad's first roommate was dying and he did so quickly. Dad ended up with a heart patient.

The rooms ringed a large activity room with tables and exercise equipment. The patients were expected to participate in activities such as Bingo or board games. Dad didn't like organized activities, be they professional sports or other useless games.

The nurses told Dad he needed to leave his room and participate as part of his treatment.

"Come on, Dad. It's good for you," I cajoled him.

"I don't want to play with these sick people. It's depressing."

Like a good inmate, he finally realized that to be released he needed to play along.

I visited him at the rehab center and we went for walks along the hallways. I held his arm as he walked.

"Aren't you mad the doctor sent you home with antibiotics when he thought you had a viral infection?"

"He made a mistake. That happens. And I did have a bacterial infection, just not one that that antibiotic worked for."

"But he should have checked you more, or done something. He was negligent. Don't you want to sue him or something?"

"I've looked at my medical records. People make mistakes, and suing them won't change what happened."

I remained surprised he wasn't a lot angrier about what happened to him. He was right, however, that suing people didn't make things better.

Before Dad could come home, he needed to complete a home visit—a trial run to see if it was possible for him to live at home with his disabilities.

We had a big sign and balloons for him. We ate lunch in our kitchen—ham sandwiches with mayo, Swiss cheese, and sweet pickles. The occupational therapist evaluated our home. She looked at the steps, the shower, the counter height, and all kinds of things. The therapist decided that there were too many steps for Dad to negotiate. Before he could come home, he needed work on that. And the steps needed a handrail. He would need an aide to help him shower and do other tasks, but these issues could be overcome.

Everyone knew that Linda and Dad weren't happily married. Dad's doctors knew, the kids knew, their friends knew. The social worker at the hospital recommended going to see a counselor or a psychologist to help them work through their problems before he moved home. They had gone to therapy years before. Dad had called Linda "frigid," at which point that round of therapy sessions had ended.

This time they first went to counseling with the priest. He had agreed to come to the hospital rehab center to see Linda and Dad. They sat in the conference room in the hospital set up for family meetings, telling our priest their problems. This priest had previously lived a monastic life in an abbey and had been at our parish for less than a year. He listened and asked questions. He wasn't well liked by the parish because, among other things, he'd told our church choir that they were horrible singers.

"Jack, it seems to me that you have a choice to make. You can either stay with your girlfriend and get a divorce, or leave your girlfriend and make amends with your lovely family. What do you want to do?"

"I can't leave my girlfriend."

The priest turned to Linda, "I know I'm not allowed to say this, but you need to get divorced."

They then went to the psychologist. Maybe Dr. Trontel, Dr. T as we came to call him, would have some ideas. He also came to the rehab center. The same story was told. Dr. T agreed. They should divorce if Dad wasn't going to leave his girlfriend.

Linda and Dad had been on a path to divorce before Dad had almost died. The illness was a red herring. The girlfriend was the real issue, or Dad's interest in having a family and a girlfriend was the issue. For a long time, he had supported two separate lives. His illness brought these two worlds together and forced him to make a decision.

After six more weeks of rehab, he was cleared to move home. And even though everyone advised that a divorce was the best way forward, he moved home. Linda still loved him.

We expected that Dad had been changed in the same way we had been by his near death experience. But he wasn't. He had been absent for most important family events up to that point, and he missed this event—our pulling together as a family while he was sick. Once he was home a few weeks, we realized this, or rather Linda did.

"Kids, we're having a family meeting in our bedroom," Linda announced. There hadn't been any yelling between Linda and Dad. They hadn't been fighting.

"Linda, help me out of the bathroom, would you?"

Linda went over and helped him get up and walk into their bedroom. Dad needed a lot of help doing even the smallest tasks.

We sat on their giant bed. The summer sun shone through the large glass windows in their room. Their two recliners, which I had never seen them sit in together, faced the large TV. Dad sat in one of the recliners. Linda stood up. Six months had passed since Gram had called me to say Dad was on his deathbed and told me to come home.

We were normally not allowed to get into their bed, but we did it when they weren't home. Here we were, though, instructed to sit there.

Once assembled, neither Linda nor Dad wanted to start talking.

"What's going on?" I asked.

"Well, kids, your father and I have decided to separate."

"You're getting a divorce?" John asked.

"We'll see," responded Dad.

"Where are you going?" Montana asked.

"I am going to stay with a friend."

"A friend? Who?" I asked.

"A friend from Portland."

Everyone knew who this friend was. He hadn't had another family, just a love interest. This is when Dad accepted the third way that was offered to him. He survived, yet decided to leave us. That's when we all realized that there had been a third option. We had to internalize that he lived but was leaving our family unit.

1997, Montana

DAD called our house one day not too long after having moved out.

Standing in the recently renovated—pre-illness—kitchen, with white cabinets and porcelain knobs, I picked up the phone when it rang. The caller ID sat on the counter next to the phone.

"Where are you calling from?" I asked. The caller ID said the call came from his girlfriend's house. I was testing him.

"I'm at a friend's house."

"What friend?"

"Chuck's."

I doodled on the pink messages pad while we spoke.

"Well, the caller ID says you're at your girlfriend's house."

"Nicole, your mom has the caller ID set up so whenever I call, it looks like I'm calling from my girlfriend's house."

I stood there wondering about this while we talked.

Is it possible that Linda reprogrammed the phone? How would she have done that? I didn't know the caller ID was programmable.

When we hung up, I called the number on the caller ID—his girlfriend's number—right back.

He answered.

"I thought you said you weren't at her house."

"I just got here."

"What? I just spoke to you. You said you were at Chuck's."

"And I just drove up."

"That's not possible."

"I told you your mom has the caller ID rigged."

"Talk to you later. I love you."

I did love him. And I wanted him to know that he could take my love for granted. No matter his behavior I still loved him. I had almost lost him.

But I was mad at him too: for lying to me, for lying to Linda, for leaving us.

I stood there in the kitchen staring at the phone. I knew he was lying and yet I wanted to believe him.

Later I asked Linda about the call.

"Can you reprogram phones to make it look like Dad was calling from his girlfriend's house even though he was someplace else?"

"No, Nicole."

"I didn't think so, but that's what Dad told me you did."

"He thinks people don't see through his lies."

"He doesn't lie to me Mom."

"Oh yes, he does. Remember when Dad brought you the Suburban last year? He had his girlfriend with him then. He left her at a rest stop while he went to exchange cars with you. He had told her he would be an hour."

"He was with me for a few hours."

Laughing she said, "I know. I love it."

I was stunned. I didn't ask Linda how she knew this story. I wish I had. It might have answered a lot of other questions, such as how long had she known about the affair? She still had friends at Delta, spies who called and gave her information, and Walt had friends, too. Maybe they had told her.

Given their previous unhappiness, their divorce shouldn't have surprised me, but it did. What didn't surprise me were their vitriolic interactions from that point forward.

The unlikely existence of their union itself had been more interesting to contemplate than its demise.

Dad's mother, Grammy Harkin had grown up in India and she cooked curry as a family staple. Dad had cooked a curry for Linda and a family legend was born. He made the curry so spicy on one date that Linda took off her blouse at the table because she was so hot. The sexual aspect of this story was lost on us children. We just laughed at the thought of Linda unbuttoning her white blouse at the table and the patent absurdity of Dad cooking. We enjoyed imagining them just meeting and having fun together, something that rarely happened in our home. After they were married Dad had been banned from the kitchen because he couldn't figure out how to clean up.

Grammy Harkin didn't have a great fondness for Linda. Dad had been her youngest and favorite son. First, Linda hadn't been Catholic when they married. Second, because Grammy Harkin was born into the upper class in

England and she felt her social status to be vastly above her current situation, Linda's family just wasn't in her social strata. And third, instead of moving back to Boston, like every other person from Boston is required to do at some point in their lives, Linda took Dad further away. All of these things, combined with Linda's natural abrasiveness, made things difficult between them.

When Linda asked for the curry recipe, Grammy Harkin gave Linda some long and convoluted recipe that took hours and hours to prepare. Linda, while an uninspired cook, eventually figured out how to make curry in under an hour. She cooked the onions and the meat together with the curry spices and then added tomatoes, potatoes, veggies, and water. Once the lid was on, it sat on the stove for a few hours. If it wasn't thick enough by dinner, she put some cornstarch in and called it done. We always had mango and lemon chutney with it. If Grammy Harkin was visiting dried shredded coconut also appeared on the table. Once a year, Linda canned and one of her best efforts was homemade spicy chutney with raisins and other fruits.

The pictures from their wedding made my parents look glamorous. Linda wore an off-white turban, with her blond hair curled up at the ends, just above her shoulders. Her off-white dress had a three-inch wide belt. She was slender and the shoes were silk platforms with her red toes poking out. She looked like a model with her false eyelashes batting. She had in fact been a model for Delta in commercials featuring flight attendants. They were married at Holy Name Cathedral in downtown Chicago, which had Gothic stained glass windows and a soaring ceiling. Linda had agreed to raise her future children Catholic in order to marry Dad there.

That Linda did this seemed odd the first time she told me that story. But as the price for getting married in the Cathedral, it hadn't seemed too onerous to her. Besides, who would be checking? But Linda always intended to honor that deal. She was like that. A done deal was a done deal. Why did Dad want us to be raised Catholic since he didn't believe? These internal contradictions confounded me.

My parents were attracted to one another because they both embraced adventure. They both liked to move. She was beautiful and well-traveled. But why they felt the need to get married was a mystery.

Maybe she wanted security and she never divorced Dad because he represented security.

Any talk of dying, in the abstract, over living in a coma, is cheap, as

Linda often said. But once Dad lived through the coma and learned that Linda had contemplated taking him off of life support, his views on plug pulling changed. Dad blamed Linda for even contemplating pulling the plug. She blamed him for everything else.

Dad did this a lot, however. He mused over something in his mind, rolling the issue or idea over and over. He did this contemplation without any input from anyone else. This was his own analysis and therefore his own conclusion which became his immutable truth. No amount of explanation or clarification changed his mind. Linda had tried to kill him. End of story.

Once he left her they both lost the ability to behave kindly towards one another. Their united front fell away. Dad didn't feel that Linda was owed anything. He had worked and therefore all of the money in his pension belonged to him.

"When is the divorce going to be over?" I asked, crying when Linda's lawyer's secretary put me through to her attorney.

"I don't know. Your father's making things difficult at every turn," he said.

This put me over the edge and into crying hysterically. He was a lawyer, not a family counselor. He didn't have the answers. He didn't know when it would be over. It would be over when it was over.

Dad hadn't gone to college and it's not clear that he graduated from high school. But I was ready to go back to college and finish.

"Dad, can you fill out the financial aid forms again for school."

"I don't have any money. I've told you that."

"But you said you'd pay for me to go to school wherever I got in. I only have three semesters left."

"Listen to me, I don't have any money."

A few days later, I took another run at things.

"Please just fill out the forms. I need the money."

"Get your mother to do it."

"She doesn't qualify. You know that."

"I'll tell you what. I'm not making any promises, but I'll talk to my girlfriend and ask to borrow the money from her for you to finish school."

Relieved, I hung up the phone. He borrowed the money for me, about ten grand. I was surprised that Dad's girlfriend would give Dad the money for me to finish college, but I didn't question it.

Back at college, I became the student I always should have been, focusing on my studies and participating in extracurricular activities.

I was on Dad's side of their divorce for the most basic of reasons: he had the money and I needed it to finish school.

"Dad, I can't find my wallet." The wallet was small and Kelly green.

"Where did you leave it?"

"I don't know," I said on the phone, panicked in my small dark dorm room. "What am I going to do?" I asked.

I was old enough to know better, old enough to deal with losing things on my own.

"You have to think back to where you lost it and find it. I can't fly out there and find it for you."

I looked out the window, from several stories up, at the courtyard below, as he said this. The phone cradled in my ear, beige cord wrapped around my arm.

I felt abandoned, but he was parenting. He wanted me to figure it out. Maybe that's one key to good parenting, every so often a child must feel abandoned.

Linda must have felt the same way, abandoned, but she had been figuring things out on her own for years. Yet, even if Dad hadn't been there all the time, they had been married. And now that they were divorcing, that backup was lost.

In reality, he had never been her support. He wasn't the person she called when something went wrong. Walt was. Thinking back, when we moved to Vancouver, one of the first questions I had was whether Walt was moving, too. He was so much a part of our life, I assumed he would move too. Maybe Dad wanted to move not only to be closer to his girlfriend but also to distance us from Walt. But that had the net effect of making life harder for Linda. And then the things that Walt had helped with, Dad needed to step up and do, but he didn't.

That was his point. Everyone deals with their problems alone.

I retraced my steps and found the wallet, right where I dropped it on the street.

The divorce broke down all of our relationships with one another. Our behaviors devolved. We became our worst selves.

Erica called me crying when I was back at school. She was living with Linda, John, Montana, and Gram. Gram had moved in to help Linda financially.

"Hey, what's going on?" I said.

"Mom kicked John out," she said. He was seventeen, a junior in high school.

"What are you talking about?"

"They had a huge fight, and she won't let him back in the house. She threw his stuff out too."

I tried to talk to Linda about what was going on.

"I've made my decision. I'm not talking to you about it," she said when I asked.

A straight answer was hard to find, but I eventually learned that John said something so mean and hurtful—something no one would repeat—that Linda kicked him out. I never found out what he said.

He ended up living with Dad in Portland to finish high school. John wanted to be a pilot.

Dad drove John to Oklahoma and dropped him off at a flight school there, summarily. He didn't give John any money or buy him any food. He just left. John was a bit panicked. Two days later, Walt appeared. He set John up: took him shopping, bought him food, did the kinds of normal things parents do when they are dropping their child off at college.

When I heard how broke John was, I started sending him five dollars a week, in a card. I was broke too, but I wanted him to know I cared. It wasn't much, but it was something.

Quickly it became apparent to John that he would not get far if he stayed at that school. His apartment was broken into repeatedly, his computer and other things stolen. By that time, Linda and John had patched up their relationship. Linda loved us too much to go too long without any of us. We were the most important things in her life. With her help, he transferred to the University of North Dakota.

Erica, sixteen at the time, sought stability outside of our family, dating a much older man. I couldn't stand him, but Linda and Dad seemed to find him to be ok. Walt hated him too. Linda and Dad were too self-absorbed to see that Erica was in crisis and needed them. She would sneak out of the house, but her grades didn't falter. Other than dating a jerk, she seemed ok on the outside.

Montana, just eleven-years-old, put his head down and tried not to cause any problems—the great peacemaker. He went to computer parties with his buddies and golfed.

After Dad's first heart attack, Dad would never be allowed to fly a plane again. He had the options of either retiring or going on long-term disability. He chose retirement, based purely on the financial calculation. But then he changed his mind, and although he had put in the paperwork with Delta, he decided it was more financially advantageous to go on long-term disability. Thus he protested his retirement. Until the retirement/disability issues were decided, he was paid nothing. That meant that neither of my parents had an income.

I still spoke to both Linda and Dad frequently.

"What do you mean we have to sell the house?"

"Your Dad isn't paying the mortgage. We don't have any money. You father isn't taking his retirement so he can try to get me to agree to less money in the divorce settlement. I'm not going to let him push me around anymore."

"But it's our house," I said.

"It's a house, like others. There'll always be another," Linda said.

Linda wouldn't budge.

"Dad, why won't you sell the house?" I asked later on the phone with him.

"Your mother won't sign the papers. It isn't up to me," Dad said.

"But we'll lose the house."

"There's nothing I can do about it."

One night Erica came home from school and found a note for her on the large wooden front doors of our home. "We moved in town. 585 2nd Ave. Love, Mom."

"We moved into town," Linda said cheerily once I finally found her new phone number by calling Walt.

"What do you mean?" I asked. I was far away at college and couldn't really comprehend that my family no longer lived in the big house.

"Where's Georgia?" Georgia was our St. Bernard.

"She's here. In the garage. With the boxes."

"What about the cats?"

"The cats are gone."

"What do you mean? Where are the cats?"

"The cats are gone," she replied.

That cryptic response was all Linda or Gram would say about the cats.

Erica and Montana didn't seem too concerned about the cats either. The trauma of the divorce had overshadowed their lives and made the cats secondary to daily survival.

When Erica had told me about finding the note, she sounded the way we all felt about our parents' antics. Unsurprised. Resigned. We couldn't do anything about it. Just as my parents had randomly moved between states while I was at camp, these kinds of things happened in our family.

Linda had come to believe that Dad had given his money to his girlfriend in preparation for his divorcing her. His getting sick hadn't been in his plan.

Linda kept seeing Dr. T, whom she and Dad had seen in the hospital, but now on her own. I had refused to see Dr. T before going back to college. I didn't need someone to help me process my life. Besides, my parents were divorcing, not me.

Dr. T helped Linda work through her feelings about Dad and the divorce. He instructed her to keep a diary, to write down in her distinctive handwriting how she was feeling. She'd taken up calligraphy when we lived in Georgia, and her writing was well formed and pleasant to look at. She journaled. She wrote all over the place, in spiral notebooks, on notepads, everywhere. She became hyper-graphic. Since she wrote everywhere, it wasn't uncommon to stumble upon these notes. She didn't try to hide them. The notes changed from processing Dad's illness to processing their relationship. Her writing took up the entire page of every page in whatever notebook she was using and the language she used was repetitive, obsessive, and manic.

The writing should have allowed her to process her relationship with Dad on paper, but it had the opposite effect. She ruminated over everything that had happened. She rehashed every twist and turn their divorce took, and then reviewed their entire marriage. She looked for signs that she'd missed. She wrote about signs she had seen, affairs that had happened earlier. Details in these notes were lacking. There were no names named.

Over winter break I came home from college for a week and promptly did my laundry. Linda taught us how to do our laundry ourselves around age ten because she didn't like washing laundry. I had dumped my clothes in our laundry room. The room held the washer and dryer, a utility sink, and our pantry of food. I started a load and walked away.

A day later, looking for my favorite brown fuzzy cashmere sweater from Benetton, I screamed, "Mom, where's my sweater?"

Linda calmly looked back at me and said, "Your behavior is

unacceptable."

I instantly became angry. My head felt like it was growing larger. I needed the sweater because I was meeting some friends. I had a taupe pleated skirt that matched the sweater perfectly.

"What do you mean?" I screamed back.

"Nicole, you heard me. Your behavior is unacceptable."

Again, screaming back, "Why do you keep saying that? And where's my sweater?"

"Your behavior is unacceptable."

"Mom, I need it. Come on," I yelled. She was starting to get through, however. My childishness could no longer be denied to myself.

She looked at me in disbelief and said, "I will be in the other room. When you want to calmly talk about this, I will be happy to do so. However, screaming at me is unacceptable."

She turned around and did just that, walked into the kitchen. I followed her in and asked again, louder, "Where's my sweater?"

I felt stupid. For so many years we had used screaming to communicate with each other, and I just couldn't stop.

Once I had calmed down, Linda explained that screaming was taking up too much of her energy, so she was stopping. If I needed something, then we needed to talk about it like adults.

The truth was that she had shrunk the sweater. She had seen the laundry on the floor as the next load that needed to be washed. She had just thrown it into the wash, and she hadn't noticed the special sweater. She had been trying to help me.

Dr. T had told her to stop screaming back. It worked.

Her screaming in my childhood had been a kind of abuse. To assert myself I had begun screaming back. We all screamed. And on this day, Linda decided to stop the cycle. She would no longer yell.

Linda still couldn't get past the fact that Dad had left her. In sessions, she hashed and rehashed what had happened. He helped her try to move on with her life, but she went over everything in her head constantly. She frequently sent me letters at college chronicling her anger and sadness.

Her letters were filled with complaints about Dad.

"Your father's at it again, up to his same old tricks. I'm glad you aren't here to see this behavior. I don't know what he is trying to achieve by abandoning his family."

While she was able to re-engineer her relationships with us, she never could get past feeling abandoned by Dad. She had stood by him through affairs, bankruptcies, and raising four children, and she couldn't grasp that he had left her.

What I think she had difficulty processing was the pattern that had emerged. She essentially had the same relationship as Gram had with her second husband—who Gram had called Mr. Miserable. For Gram, life had been good, and then there was a huge upheaval. Prison. After that, things had never gone back to what they had been. Gram had divorced her husband because he had accused her of having an affair while he was in prison. But he just wasn't happy with her, just like Dad hadn't been happy with Linda. Both couples made for good partnerships but lacked love.

Linda and Mr. Miserable had eventually stopped talking. He had sent her and her siblings a letter telling them he was done with them and never wanted to speak to them again. He sent those letters because Linda had taken her sister to their local bank to get a loan for her sister to go to college. Mr. Miserable hadn't approved of my aunt's college choice, and he was also deeply embarrassed that his children had gone behind his back in their small town to borrow money. So he cut off contact with them.

I've read that women either pick "dicks" or "dads." The dicks are the fun guys who aren't ready to settle down and parent. The dads are men who are natural caregivers and helpers, who are ready to be parents. The women in my family are drawn to the dicks, but the dicks—even when they become dads—cause the most trouble.

What would have helped Linda move past things with Dad would have been to sit down with him and talk about things rationally, to have done an unemotional debriefing.

"I loved you," Dad could have said.

"I loved you too," Linda could have said.

"We just weren't right for each other at the end of the day," they could have said in unison.

"When you had an affair, it made me sad," she could have said.

"But you weren't warm towards me after the kids were born and we moved to the lake," he could have replied.

"I felt abandoned in the middle of nowhere. That wasn't what I had signed up for," she could have said.

"I am sorry you were unhappy and I should have responded differently,"

Dad could have said.

"Me too."

"Thank you for raising such wonderful children," he might have said.

"We'll be friends, for the kids. We can do that, can't we?" she might have asked.

"Maybe not friends, but a truce. For the kids," he could have said.

But neither of them could do it. Instead, they fought, screaming at each other through their lawyers and the courts for the rest of Linda's life. Fighting was such a part of their relationship that it was, at that final point, the only thing left between them. However, Linda was determined not to be left with zero after twenty-five years together.

1998, Montana

THE state of Montana is a community property state and, as such, any property Linda and Dad had acquired during their marriage needed to be split equally between them in their divorce.

The only large assets remaining by the time their divorce went to court were Dad's pension from Delta and Linda's rings. He preferred to whittle away his money on lawyer's fees rather than give Linda any money. This situation sounds contrived like it's from a movie or a novel, but as their child, living through two people disentangling their lives with a distinct lack of agency in the process, the situation moved quickly into nightmare territory.

Dad's next step in the divorce was to file for bankruptcy. Before settling their divorce the local court needed to wait until the bankruptcy court ruled on Dad's bankruptcy. Generally, a primary residence and retirement money are beyond the reach of bankruptcy courts. However, because our whole family had moved out, our home no longer received this protection. The old house was foreclosed on days after Linda moved into town.

The bankruptcy court was charged with figuring out whether Dad could pay his debts. If not, then his debts would be discharged. If so, well, then no discharge. Dad and Linda submitted many years of documents to the court. The looming question was where had Dad's money gone? What had he done with this massive salary? This process took months.

Linda's attorney was crafty and he petitioned the bankruptcy court and the local court for her to receive her part of Dad's lump sum retirement while Dad and the courts figured things out.

Dad's attorney hadn't expected the court to grant this request, but the judge did so. The first money to come out of Dad's lump sum retirement money was tax-free, creating a windfall for Linda. She was done waiting in poverty. She had used this money to buy cars for her and Erica and to buy the new house in town.

The bankruptcy court allowed his bankruptcy to go through even though the court couldn't account for where Dad's money had gone.

When we had first moved to Montana, I couldn't figure out the local TV. The news seemed so unpolished, as though a few people decided to stand in front of a camera and talk about stuff. There weren't any smooth transitions out to the field and back to the studio. The local court in our town was similarly small and maybe seemed similarly unpolished to Dad so maybe that's why he didn't expect what happened next.

Dad told the judge in their divorce, "Your honor, I'm a very sick man. I don't have long to live. Paying Linda alimony for twelve years isn't possible. I'm too sick to do this. I won't live that long."

As Linda told me Dad said this, I worried about Dad. Didn't he think he would live for twelve years? How could that be? No one I loved had died yet in my life. My parents dying was as foreign a concept to me as scuba diving in Antarctica, even though Dad had previously almost died. I hadn't expected Dad to die when he had been sick. And, against most everyone else's expectations, he hadn't.

During all of this, I was still in college. The library had a large bound book listing internships available to students in the US. I stood at the printer in the basement of the library and copied any page that had an interesting internship. I then pasted the small cutouts of internships into a little spiral bound notebook with an orange cover so I could apply to them.

The orange cover belied the interesting opportunities inside. I needed some experience to go with my political science degree or as Dad called it underwater basket weaving. I applied to internships in Washington, D.C., Montana, and Chicago. The unpaid internship in Chicago was entry level but working on government oversight.

I called to follow-up on the position.

"Who the hell are you?" said the person on the other end of the phone.

I repeated myself.

"Where the hell are you from?"

"I'm from Montana."

"Montana? I love Montana. What's your name again, kid?"

I told him and we chatted amicably.

Weeks later, the offer came in the mail. I had spoken to the Executive Director that day. Excited about this opportunity, I called Dad immediately to tell him. Working for a non-profit on government oversight meant adding sorely needed experience to my resume. I had found something interesting to do with my political science degree.

"So the job's unpaid?"

"Yes, but it'll give me some work experience."

"You can't work for free. Come home to Montana and work at the fuel station to make some money."

"This is pretty exciting, Dad. I think I should take the internship. They don't have that many of them."

"You already owe my girlfriend for paying for your school. You're an adult and you can do what you want, but I won't give you any more money until you pay her back."

"But *you* borrowed the money. I didn't borrow it."

"I borrowed the money for you. You knew that."

"But *you* said you would pay for my college."

"I'm not giving you any more money."

Historically, Dad had used money to get me to do what he thought was best. Telling him that I wasn't working in Montana for the summer—that I wasn't letting him control me anymore—meant a fundamental shift in our relationship. This marked the beginning of the end. Either I did what he said, or he wouldn't help me.

The crux of our disagreement was this: he thought I should repay his girlfriend for the money he had borrowed from her for me to go to school. I felt I didn't owe her anything. She was the reason for my parent's divorce. She was the easiest person to blame.

Dad equated giving someone money with loving them. I had to decide if I wanted his love. Messy rooms or dirty cars showed disrespect for our possessions—which he had paid for—and this messiness thereby disrespected his hard work. He grew up so poor that material possessions in his family had represented a proxy for love.

I thought that if I could show him that I could do it on my own, that I could live without his financial support, then that might be enough to prove to him that I was capable of making my own decisions. We could have a relationship independent of money and we could relate to each other as adults and enjoy each other's company. But after he said "no" to helping me, the first thing I did was call my mom. I wasn't quite independent yet.

When I told Linda what Dad said, she wasn't surprised. She called my aunt who lived in Chicago and asked if I could live with her. My aunt's apartment fascinated me. She had masquerade party masks hung on the wall for decoration and a large poster of stones above her chairs in her living room. Unfortunately for me, my aunt had cats. And, like Linda, she never had any food in her fridge, but she let me live there for free.

The cats didn't bother me much because I was barely there that summer. I worked a lot—nine to five everyday downtown at my unpaid internship in the Carbon and Carbide building on Michigan Avenue. My aunt gave me her hostess job at the corner restaurant Friday and Saturday nights. She knew the owners. I was paid eight bucks an hour, two drinks a night, and dinner. They served an amazing chicken pasta with sun-dried tomatoes that I ate with my vodka tonic. Sunday through Thursday evenings I worked for Blockbuster video, telling people which movies to rent and which to avoid. And Saturdays and Sundays, I worked at a garden center, outside, selling pansies and watering everything in the hot Chicago summer. I clipped coupons and ate peanut butter and Nutella sandwiches for lunch.

The repo guy called me while I was living in Chicago.

"Ms. Harkin, your father gave me your number. I need to take possession of your Suburban."

"When?"

"As soon as possible."

"Um, well I need the car a few more days. Can you call me back? I would really appreciate it."

I needed the car to get around Chicago to all of my different jobs.

He called again a few weeks later.

"Hi, Ms. Harkin. How's your summer going?"

"Well. Loving Chicago. I guess you want the car?"

"I do. I do."

"Could you hold off another week?"

"Well, I need to get it back."

By this point, the car was both unregistered and uninsured, like me.

"I just need to move my stuff back to school. Then I will give it to you. Next week?"

He waited a few more weeks to call me back. And finally, it was the end of the summer. I didn't need the Suburban anymore. I was always polite and always answered the phone when he had called. Maybe that's why he played this game with me all summer. Finally, we set a time and date to meet up. It was the day I left Chicago. I removed my Montana license plates, handed over the keys to the guy, and took the 'L' to the airport. A friend later told me that I was the only person he had ever heard of who succeeded in negotiating with the repo man. Dad had always said, "You get more bees with honey than with vinegar."

After my summer working in Chicago, I had two semesters of school left to graduate, but I didn't have the money to finish.

And even though I had proven to Dad that I could make it on my own and hadn't needed his money over the summer to do so, he refused to give me any more money. Like Linda, he remained consequential—he told me he wouldn't give me any more money because I had chosen to take an unpaid internship in Chicago instead of working at the fuel station to repay his wife.

In that moment, when Dad told me he would not ever help me again, I felt like he was dishonoring his agreement to send me to college.

I wanted to be able to say no to him, to his requirements, while at the same time still having him fund my life. My wants were a bit unrealistic.

Linda didn't have any credit history and therefore could not take out student loans and she didn't feel financially secure enough to pay for my college tuition with cash.

Just like how I had to figure out where my wallet had gone, I needed to figure out how to finish college on my own.

As I had done every year on the first day of the school year I got up at 4:15 a.m. to stand in line at the financial aid office to see a financial aid counselor. I did it so I wouldn't have to stand in the line all day. If I got there early, I would be at the beginning of the line.

I took a number and waited yet again inside the counselor's office. The building was one of the oldest on campus. The hallways were large and the building was stone. I was called into the office and sat next to the counselor's desk.

I cried while handing the counselor the letter I had written explaining everything. My dad's illness, the divorce, and finally that I didn't have any parental support for my final year of school. Walt, our family friend, had agreed to co-sign a student loan with me, but this still left me a few thousand dollars short. Without the help of the college, I wouldn't be able to graduate.

The woman read the letter and then asked me to wait there.

"I'm so sorry about crying," I said when she returned.

"It's OK. You've been through a lot. I think we can help you."

The school gave me a grant for the few thousand dollars I still needed to pay my tuition. I worked at the library to pay my rent and food money.

Begging for money to finish school went a long way toward ending my sense of entitlement. Dad had money, but his money was no longer my money.

Eventually, the judge in Linda and Dad's divorce ruled creatively and explained that since Dad presented information to the court about his frail state, she had to take him at his word. To ensure that Linda had enough money, even if Dad died, the judge ordered Dad to pay Linda her maintenance in a lump sum rather than monthly. The judge was savvier than he had expected.

Dad appealed this ruling to the Supreme Court of Montana, which was the only court to which he could appeal. Even so, the divorce dragged on and on until the Supreme Court sided with Linda. Dad finally seemed out of options.

No matter whether or not Dad had planned for years to divorce Linda or it had just happened because of his illness, Linda won. She received her fair and equitable portion of the estate they had built together. Yes, he made the income, but Linda ran the home and the court recognized this.

Linda receiving all of her money first without paying taxes was unfair, but Dad had not been playing fair. It seemed like he got his just deserts.

However, Dad still wanted Linda's wedding rings. Even though Dad had lost, he didn't give up. Perseverance may be a personality trait that leads to success. In this instance, it just led to more and more heartbreak.

Linda held on to what she could: her children. Montana wanted a cat, but I was allergic to cats. Montana picked out the cat and brought it home. He loved that kitty.

"But Linda, I'm allergic."

"Do you know why I got Montana that cat? Because he's not going anywhere without that cat, and that cat lives here. Buying love, Nicole. Buying love."

As it turned out, Linda was the one who would leave.

1998, Washington, D.C. & Montana

NOT long after they moved to town Erica called to tell me Gram and Linda weren't speaking. After Linda and Dad's gigantic divorce drama, Linda and Gram broke up too.

"What?"

"Gram's moving out."

"Erica, what are you talking about?"

"After dinner, Mom asked Gram to bring in the hot dog buns on the patio, and then they were fighting."

Gram and Linda stopped talking because of hot dog buns, after so many years together.

"Do you have any idea about what happened?" I asked.

"Well, they might have been fighting about Walt," she said.

Walt had moved to Montana. He lived in a small two-bedroom apartment not far from our house.

"What about him?"

"I know you don't want to hear this, but Gram was upset that he and Mom are dating," Erica said.

"No, they aren't," I said.

"Yes, they are. Get over it. Gram wants her to date other men. She doesn't think Walt is good enough for Mom."

My brain was already off. I couldn't hear anything Erica had said. It just couldn't be true. But when I went home the next time, Linda made tacos, one of her staples.

"Linda, why'd you get soft tacos? I like the corn tacos better."

"So did your father. Walt prefers the soft tacos," said Linda.

After she moved out, Gram became the gypsy she was meant to be. She traveled the country staying with friends and family, trying to decide where to settle down. She spent two years on the road, between time in California and Colorado. She ended up in Williamstown, Massachusetts, with my uncle.

Linda and Gram were both too stubborn and angry to get over it. Neither of them budged. After so many years together, and too many unresolved issues, they dissolved their relationship.

But what makes someone think they can just stop having a relationship with their child? Or, makes a child stop relating to their parent? I was heartbroken that they kept fighting.

Gram felt strongly about how things should be done and if Linda didn't do things properly, she was in the wrong, which garnered Gram's intense displeasure. Linda wanted to live her life without Gram's judgment. They landed in a catch-22, a stalemate, where neither was willing to relent.

I knew this about these women. Neither of them said, "I'm sorry" often. I had learned that saying I was sorry, even if I wasn't sorry about my behavior, but was sorry about the disagreement, generally, was the easiest way to avoid these types of stalemates. Just apologize and move on.

Linda and I chatted often, almost every day, so her call that day wasn't a surprise.

"Your father's trying to get an annulment," Linda said on the phone from her kitchen.

"Why?" I asked from my desk in my office.

"So he can marry his girlfriend."

"You were married for twenty-five years and have four children together. I don't think the Church will fall for that."

I had moved to Washington D.C. during my last semester of college for an internship with one of the Senators from Montana and stayed.

"Why is he asking for an annulment? He never even went to church."

Had Dad's near death experience changed his views on religion? No. The actual reason was he wanted to somehow invalidate their marriage. He wanted some authority to tell him that his marriage to Linda hadn't been real, that he hadn't spent years married to a woman he didn't love.

What would an annulment mean for us kids? If our parent's marriage was annulled, would we become illegitimate? Was he also trying to disavow us? Hadn't he wanted children? Us?

Seeking to have their marriage annulled meant not only did he not want to be with us, his family, but he also wanted to pretend that we didn't exist, hadn't been a family. I suppose he sat on reserve in Portland for years, doing just that, pretending we didn't exist. That sounds like something Linda would say.

The annulment wasn't allowed, but he did remarry.

I wasn't invited, nor were John or Erica. Only Montana was there. Dad's divorce attorney performed the ceremony. I feel like someone told me they were married near the river in Missoula, but maybe I made that detail up. My uncle and aunt, Dad's brother and sister-in-law were in attendance as well. And then Dad's girlfriend changed into his wife. She took our last name. There were then two Mrs. Harkin's.

That spring, I called Linda.

"Mom, are you coming to graduation?"

I was flying back to Indiana for the ceremony.

"Is your father coming?" she asked.

"Maybe."

"I can't afford to come," she said.

This same conversation played itself out with Dad. Neither of them could afford it.

I called Gram, crying.

"No one's coming to my graduation."

"What do you mean?" she asked.

"Mom and Dad both say they can't afford to come."

"I guess I'll come then," Gram said.

At least someone would be there. For a few weeks, I was sad and embarrassed that neither of my parents were coming.

But then Linda changed her mind. She decided to come with Walt and Montana. Not to be outdone by Linda, Dad changed his mind, too. He came with his wife. Gram hadn't needed to come after all.

"You missed a fun ride in Business Class," Walt told me after they arrived.

"What do you mean?"

"The gate agent saw four Harkins traveling on free passes and thought they were together, so your mother, Montana, and your father and his wife sat together in one row. Your Dad and his two wives. I sat behind them."

"What did they talk about?"

"Hell, I don't know, Nicole, but I bet the flight attendants were confused."

After graduation, I went back to Washington, D.C. to start my career.

1999, Missouri

I met Mr. Miserable once. Before the internet, the Library of Congress kept the phone books for all of the US in one place. I had noticed the phone books when I was there working on a documentary about Asians in Montana at the turn of the 20th century. Every day I searched the photography collection for images of Asian men or women working on the railroad in Montana. To find Mr. Miserable, I looked him up at the Library of Congress. It hadn't been that difficult. I had always assumed he would be unfindable.

Standing in my apartment's small galley kitchen, I dialed the number. Surely it wouldn't be him. A woman answered.

Through sudden and unexpected tears I said, "Hi. This is Nicole Harkin. I am looking for Ed Epping. He's my grandfather." I couldn't believe that I was so emotional about someone I had never met. I kept on, "He was married to Eve Murry. Do I have the right number?"

"Ed, someone's on the phone for you," said his wife. He had remarried after divorcing Gram.

My grandfather and I chatted. He seemed kind. He invited me to come visit.

Out visiting Gram a few months later, I told her I was going to meet Mr. Miserable. Gram had moved back to her hometown St. Louis by then, just an hour away from his home by car.

He was almost blind when I met him. Glaucoma. I didn't ask him any of the big questions. Why did you cut off contact with your whole family? Did you miss them? Did you miss us? Did you even know what you missed?

"I met your father once. I liked him," he said as we chatted.

"Oh. Yes, he can be charming."

"What are your brothers and sister like?"

"Well, they're in school. John's studying to be a pilot, like my dad. Erica's in high school and has a serious boyfriend. Montana's into computers."

"What about your mom?"

I choked as he asked. "She's good. She's taking computer classes at the community college and likes her new house."

"What do you do?" he asked.

"I just started a new job working for a nonprofit, investigating misuse of government funds."

It's funny that I became interested in government oversight before I knew about my grandfather's prison stint for embezzlement of government funds. I liked the sense of justice inherent in the work, the sense that I was righting wrongs.

We sat in their sunroom overlooking the golf course and the artificial lake they lived on. There were white swans in the pond.

I stood up to go to the bathroom. His wife asked me to help her with something in the kitchen.

"He's missed you."

"Oh. Thank you for saying that."

"He's such a kind man. I don't know what went on with everything."

But once he had sent a letter like that cutting off all contact, he couldn't undo it and go back.

As I was leaving, he asked me to visit again. The whole time I was there I felt I was betraying Gram by spending time with this man who had so hurt her.

When I returned to Gram's apartment, she begrudgingly peppered me with questions about him and their house.

"What did his house look like?"

"It was in a development and looked out onto a pond."

"Well, let's get ready to go to dinner."

On the way to dinner, "How did he look? Does he look old?"

"I guess so. You look better than him."

"Where should we get dinner? What did his wife look like?"

Gram wanted to know more about him, and yet she didn't. Their divorce was a taboo in our family, something we weren't supposed to even to allude to. Only much later did I realize that Gram didn't get anything in their divorce but her dining room set, her four white chairs, coffee table, and bed. No alimony, no support, nothing else. After twenty-five years together, sticking by him through prison, she got nothing. At fifty-years-old, she had started from zero, yet again.

The parallels between the choices Linda and Gram made can't be denied. They both married smart, self-made men who ended up screwing them. Then they divorced and their husbands cut off contact with their children because they could no longer control them.

1999, Washington, D.C. & Montana

LINDA surprised me again.

"Over Easter, I'm converting," she said on the phone.

She was becoming Catholic.

"Really?"

"I've always wanted to be a Eucharistic minister," Linda said.

A Eucharistic minister is a lay position. They give the parishioners wine during the service standing on the altar next to the priest who is handing out waifers and blessing people as they come up.

For the year prior she had attended religious education classes with a group of other aspirant Catholics without telling me. She went through First Communion and knew the Stations of the Cross. She learned the things about Catholicism I had supposedly been learning for years in religious education.

Linda believed in God and Catholicism. She believed more than any of the rest of us. She felt serving as a Eucharistic minister was her "calling."

When I complained to Linda about always having to call her, Linda told me she didn't want to interfere with my life and instead of calling me occasionally, she sent me checks with "phone calls" in the memo section. We talked the same amount, but her checks said she knew calling her was expensive and she wanted to help. But how would her calling me have interfered with my life? What was she talking about? Did she feel Gram had interfered with her life?

A horrible flu had kept Linda sick in bed for a month, but she was finally over it. Every time I called her, I asked the same thing, "Did I wake you up?"

"No," she replied every time.

"But you sound so tired."

I asked her so often that we started joking about it.

Normally when I called her, I was asking for money. I wasn't making ends meet with my paycheck. The last time I asked, the call went a little differently.

"Can I ask a favor? I know I do this every month, but this time is the last time. I am about to bounce a check and I was wondering if maybe you could go down to the bank and put in a hundred bucks for me? Trust me, Linda, I won't ever do it again."

Normally, I gave Linda an accounting of my spending and she replied that this was the last time, but she would do it. I didn't want to be dependent on my single mom, but I couldn't get my spending habits to align with my income.

"Have I ever told you the 'trust me joke'?" Linda asked.

"No."

"It goes something like this, 'Trust me, the check's in the mail, I'll respect you in the morning, and I won't cum in your mouth.'"

"MOM, I have to go." I hung up.

I couldn't believe that Linda had just said that to me. I ran down the hall to a co-worker's office and told him the joke. He laughed and laughed, slapping his leg.

Linda must have had the joke ready for my call. I was certain it was Walt's idea.

Fifteen minutes later, after I was over my shock about Linda not only knowing about such things but also about bringing these unmentionables up to me on the phone, I called her back.

"Mom, I get your point, but about that money..."

That was, however, the last time I called Linda for money. She was signaling that the tap was dry. Unless I wanted to hear Linda tell me more sex jokes, I needed to find another spigot. I found a night job at Starbucks.

1999, Banff, Canada

THROUGH my job I received a grant to attend a conference in Banff, Canada. We were investigating the Nuclear Regulatory Commission and its lack of response to a gigantic pile of mined uranium waste sitting next to and leaching into the Colorado River. I hoped to use NAFTA to get the government to take action, hence my attendance at a NAFTA conference. My first business trip and for international travel nonetheless. Banff was only a six-hour drive from Kalispell, so I hatched a plan to fly to Kalispell, pick up Linda and Erica, and then drive to Banff. They could have a vacation while I went to the conference.

Driving to Banff took us through the mountains of western Canada. Naturally, we stopped when we saw the sign for Mt. Harkin, but the clouds hung low in a late summer cold snap and obscured the mountains.

Linda spent most of our trip in the crappy little hotel room. That was strange. Normally she would have been out and about looking at things—touristing as I called it. Instead, she was sleeping a lot and smoking on the balcony hotel room. And sleeping. And smoking.

On the way home from Banff, we saw a sign for some hot springs so we stopped to check them out. Linda loved hot springs.

"Let's go in," said Linda.

"We don't have time or swimsuits and my flight's tomorrow morning from Kalispell. We have to get home."

"It won't take that long."

"We just can't. Let's go next time."

Erica took my photo with Linda in front of the hot springs. I was a head shorter than Linda and her legs were so skinny. Then we drove on, never visiting these or any other hot springs again. In the picture, her neck had a slight bulge, and her face was puffy, something only noticeable upon reflection.

1999-2000, Montana

WALT called me at home in Washington, D.C., a few months later. Outside it was cold with Thanksgiving right around the corner.

"Nicole, now I don't want you to worry, but Linda went to the doctor because she's got something growing on her neck," Walt said.

"What are you talking about?" I asked.

"Look, they put her on antibiotics for now, and are going to do a biopsy next week."

Choking a bit, unable to swallow, I looked at the denim couch from Ikea.

"Is it cancer?" This flew out of my mouth before I had time to think about what I was asking.

I had always expected to get this call, knowing that life would drastically change again some day. I expected the call because she smoked so much and had done so for so long. When I was in first grade Linda had worked on the school play, "Pinocchio, Don't Smoke That Cigarette." I can remember watching her build giant cigarettes for the set while smoking. She had always smoked.

Walt slowly said, "They don't know yet."

"How long has this thing been there?"

"For a few months. I tried to get her to go to the doctor, but she wouldn't go. She's just been wearing scarves to cover it up. I finally told her she had to go to the doctor before Thanksgiving or I was leaving her."

Walt and Linda were together. Walt, the man who I never wanted as a father, remained. Solid. Reliable. Constant. And he was now on the phone telling me that my mom was sick.

I hung up the phone, scared. I didn't want my mom to be sick. I just wanted life to be normal. Why was this happening, I wondered? Why now? Hadn't we been through enough? Hadn't I? Who in the universe was responsible for this? Who could I yell at? This just wasn't fair.

It had felt like life was finally getting back to normal. The divorce seemed over. Erica and Montana were in high school. John was doing well at college. Walt was going to culinary school at the local community college and Linda continued taking computer classes there, too.

As that thought about fairness popped into my head, I heard Dad's words, "Life isn't fair." I understood what those words meant. I didn't get credit for having had one sick parent. I didn't get credit for my parent's epic divorce. I couldn't expect fairness.

I called Gram to tell her Linda was sick. They still weren't talking. Gram called Linda but Linda refused to talk to her.

"Mom, you have to talk to her. She's your mother."

"I don't have to talk to her."

And that's where things stood.

A few weeks later after the biopsy, the doctors knew Linda had cancer, but not what kind.

"What should I do?" I asked Walt.

"It's up to you."

"Let me talk to Linda." Linda picked up the phone. "Mom, are you OK?" I asked.

"I'm fine."

"Are you still smoking? Do you want me to come home?" I asked.

"Just stay calm. Let's see what happens."

She ignored my first question.

"What else did the doctor say? Where did the cancer come from?"

"I don't know."

"What kind of treatment is there?"

"I don't know. I'm giving the phone to back to Walt."

"Wait, I need more information. Did this have something to do with your thyroid problem?"

"Nicole, not everyone is an investigator and asks a million questions."

My office was closed the week of Christmas so I could have waited until then, just a few weeks later, but I decided to go home right away. Walt gave me a pass to fly home standby.

Once I arrived in Montana, I went to appointments with Linda. I had a laundry list of questions to ask.

Linda's oncologist asked to have a family meeting. She was short and had brown hair. We filed into her sterile office. The fluorescent lights cast a slightly blue hue over everything. There weren't enough chairs so only Linda was sitting while Erica, Walt, Montana, and I stood behind her. John was still at college.

"Her cancer's aggressive. We don't know where it originated. Without this knowledge, we don't know which chemo will work best to arrest its development."

I started in with questions. "How can you figure that out?"

"Linda waited so long to come in that we may never know where the cancer came from."

That felt like a rebuke from the doctor, who never even asked why Linda hadn't come in as soon as she first felt the bump.

The doctor reported that even though Linda was a prolific smoker her lungs were clear. She didn't have lung cancer. She also didn't have breast or colon cancer. None of the usual suspects seemed to be to blame.

The chemo they would use was untested. The radiation would target the large tumor on her neck.

Everyone was looking someplace other than at the doctor, at the windows behind her, or her degrees on the wall. She went on.

"This isn't good. I generally like to give my patients and their families more information than I have for you."

"But what do you think? Can you cure her?" I asked.

"We can't cure her."

"But you must have some idea?"

"At the outside, I would estimate that she has six months to live. This is if we're very aggressive with the chemo and radiation, and she responds to the chemo."

I couldn't process this information. I stopped talking and thinking. To keep thinking would have led me to the realization that Linda would be dead before the end of summer.

Back in the car, everyone was silent.

"I need you to do some shopping for me when we get home," Linda said. She was trying to change the subject. "I want to get my Christmas shopping done."

She hadn't gone to the doctor when she noticed the growth on her neck because she was scared Dad would take Erica and Montana away from her. Montana was fourteen and an eighth grader. Erica was seventeen. Custody of children could be changed, and she couldn't bear to lose Montana or Erica.

A few weeks later, Linda's radiologist wanted to discuss her weight, so Linda and I headed to the hospital. This doctor was grave and her dark hair and clothing were conservative.

"You've lost about eight pounds since beginning treatment. Have you been eating?"

"Yes, but nothing tastes good."

In reality, Linda hadn't been eating much. The radiation was burning her mouth. All she wanted was ice.

"I think we need to talk about a stomach tube," said the doctor.

"What's that?" I asked.

Dad had never needed one of those when he had been sick. Like the chemo and radiation, this was yet more new medical territory for us.

"The stomach tube would allow Linda to maintain her weight without eating. She can receive liquid nourishment. Would you mind talking to the doctor who 'installs' them?"

Linda looked defeated. Her shoulders were slumped and her khaki pants and white button-up hallmark blouse were a little wrinkled. Because her neck was so burnt from her radiation treatments, she wasn't wearing her trademark pearl necklace nor the green emerald necklace Walt had given her years earlier.

I wouldn't have even made it to the doctor that day had our roles been reversed.

"Is the doctor who puts these tubes in a good cook?" Linda asked.

I smiled as we waited for the doctor to smile at the joke.

"Well, Linda I don't know anything about his cooking," the confused doctor replied.

Linda made a sound that was an all-purpose response for her. While exhaling, she put her tongue at the top of her closed mouth. It sounded like a comma would have sounded, "chu." Her head bounced back a bit and she exhaled while she said it—there was a physicality to the word.

I make the sound, too. It almost means, "yeah, right" without the snottyness. Erica makes the noise when she speaks as well.

"She's kidding. It's a joke," I explained. Linda's dry sense of humor had no effect on the doctor. The tension remained in the room.

Of course, we assented to the feeding tube.

Losing your appetite is an early sign of death. If you don't eat, you will die, but I didn't know this then.

Linda also had a line in place so she could receive chemo twenty-four hours a day. The chemo made her lethargic, nauseated, and she looked like she wanted to give up on life. Maybe life was giving up on her, but she kept going to make us happy. Press on, as she said.

Linda told me where to go and what to buy for Christmas that year. Together we ordered gifts online and I went to Costco for other things. Shirts for Walt and coddled eggcups in royal blue and white for Gram and Linda's aunt. Not tons of gifts, but a few. She wouldn't speak to Gram, but she sent her a Christmas gift.

On Christmas morning Erica, John, Montana, Walt, and I woke up, dressed, sat in front of the tree, and were sad. Finally, Linda emerged from her bedroom. On Christmases-past Linda required that we get dressed before any gifts were opened. This had given her and Dad a little more time to sleep and made the photos look more professional. But this year, she sat on the teal- and peach-colored plaid couch in her robe, in front of the short tree that could only fit a fraction of our ornament collection, watching us open presents. She smoked a cigarette and drank coffee with half and half and opened the presents from us. A new silk robe from me.

She smiled as we opened the presents, but she seemed troubled. She was worrying about us and how we would survive without her. And she was in pain. A lot more pain than we realized.

I made waffles as was the tradition on Christmas morning, but Linda went back to bed before she ate any.

Six days later on the New Year's Eve of the new millennium, Linda said, "I can't feel my legs."

"I'm sure it's nothing. You haven't been out of bed much. Your muscles are atrophying. We'll do more walking tomorrow."

"OK."

I knew about muscles atrophying because Dad's muscles had done that when he was sick. He had lain in bed so long, his muscles lost much of their mass. I thought this was happening to Linda.

I left and headed to my friends' house to see her and her family in their log cabin home. We played Trivial Pursuit and laughed. I worried that I was spending my mother's last New Year's with my friends, but I also desperately wanted things to be normal. I wanted Linda to be at home and well.

Early the next morning Linda asked for help going to the bathroom.

"I still can't get my legs to work."

"Come on, Mom. You're just a little tired."

"No, you aren't listening to me. I can't stand up."

I picked her up under her arms thinking standing might help her walk. It didn't. Linda almost fell in the bathroom doorway, but I was strong enough to hold her. I yelled to Walt for help. Light from the bathroom streamed into her bedroom. I maneuvered her to her peach patterned bedroom chair.

I called her oncologist's office and explained the situation.

"Could this have something to do with the cancer?" I asked.

"Absolutely not. This isn't my area. Please call 911 if you think you need to," said the doctor on call.

It was New Year's Day and maybe he was hungover or maybe he didn't believe me, but he sure made me feel like an ass for calling him. I had no choice though since she couldn't walk. I called 911.

At the hospital, the ER doctors quickly established that Linda's spine was broken and it was, in fact, a cancer tumor that broke it.

A broken back isn't normally something that's associated with smoking. People think they understand the risk they're taking when they smoke, the risk of lung cancer. However, sometimes you get other cancers and these cancers can't be treated because the doctors can't figure out where the cancer started. Then your back breaks.

Linda received morphine.

"Your mother has two options," the young spine surgeon explained. He was wearing jeans, untied high-tops, and his haircut made him look a bit like Woody Woodpecker. But he had a reputation as an excellent neurosurgeon.

"First, she can decide not to have back surgery. In that case, she will never walk again or have control over her bodily functions. The second option is for me to repair her spine. She may then walk again, but I can't make any promises. She could also die during the operation."

I took this in. Neither option was good. Walt and I turned to Linda.

"Mom, what do want to do? Surgery or nothing?" I asked her while holding her hand.

I wasn't clear that Linda understood the options because she was so out of it on the pain drugs they were giving her.

So many people are stricken with cancer that we have some collective idea of what to expect. It's the unexpected that makes remaining resilient in the face of crisis hard.

"Let's do it," she said.

I called Father Kevin from the hospital. He was our new priest who I had yet to meet. After I explained how sick Linda was, I asked him through tears to come by. I didn't believe but I still found comfort from the Church and Linda definitely believed.

When he arrived he blessed Linda and had a generally calming effect. He explained that if anything were to happen to Linda, she remained in a state of grace and would be received as thus by God. Just hearing this made me feel better. I was so scared.

Waiting for Linda was similar to waiting for Dad. We played cards again and watched the TV. I went home to shower and then Walt went home. There was almost a sense of *déjà vu* about the scene—we had been there before, but this time we had more knowledge of what might happen. She might die. We weren't in the same hospital waiting but it seemed the same. We had known she was sick but a broken back had not been on the menu.

Hours later the doctor came bounding out of the surgery to us. He told the five of us—Walt, John, Erica, Montana, and I—that Linda did great in the surgery. Pleased, he told us she had lost almost no blood during the surgery.

"I thought we might lose her, but she came through with flying colors."

He spoke as though Linda had had some agency in the outcome.

Rationally, this surgery shouldn't have been undertaken. The doctors knew she was mortally ill with cancer. The broken back was a symptom of this illness. While the surgery did give her some measure of life quality, the doctors could tell she was going to die soon. Contrary to this, the success of the surgery gave us hope that the doctors were wrong, again.

The next morning, on January 2, 2000, a woman from the business office in the hospital came into Linda's hospital room. She wore a suit and carried a clipboard. Linda was still in the ICU. The woman tried to start a conversation with the heavily drugged and intubated Linda.

"Linda, do you have some alternate form of insurance? We were informed by your insurance carrier that your coverage has been canceled."

I frantically motioned to the woman to follow me into the hallway. Linda hadn't heard a thing.

"Under no circumstances are you to discuss this with my mom. Talk to me. Can't you see how sick she is?"

"I'm sorry, but I need to know how she plans to pay for her hospital stay."

"I'll look into it and get back to you."

My first thought was to call Dad screaming. He'd canceled her insurance. That was a new low in the annals of their divorce. What kind of person canceled the insurance of someone with cancer? How could he have done this to her? Was he really so heartless?

I called the insurance company instead. My anger at Dad had been misplaced. He hadn't canceled her insurance. A real-life Y2K bug had snagged Linda. The insurance company hadn't reloaded the tape with her insurance coverage back into the mainframe computer after the New Year. Thankfully she still was insured.

2000, Montana

EVEN though Linda had cancer and it seemed like everything was on hold, life didn't stop. Walt took care of Linda and Linda worked on healing. Montana went to school. Erica managed the old-timey movie theater in town and took classes at the community college. John returned to college. In fact, however, life for us was rapidly changing, even if we couldn't quite see it. Indeed, we chaffed under the forced togetherness. We hadn't lived together in one house for a long time.

Erica and I drove around town in Erica's blue Chevy Blazer. She continued to date the gross guy I couldn't stand. He was snotty, unattractive, and not kind to Erica.

"The worst thing that could happen while Linda is sick would be for you to get pregnant," I lectured Erica in the car.

"I'm not having sex. You know this."

"I'm just saying go see the doctor and get on the pill. It's no big deal."

"Fine."

A few weeks later, Erica and I went to Washington, D.C. to put my belongings into storage. I had given up the room because I couldn't pay my rent if I wasn't working. Erica coming to D.C. to help me was a kind gesture. Things for her hadn't been easy. Linda and Dad were preoccupied with their divorce and since Erica was almost of age, they didn't fight over her. Erica had decided to live with Linda and that was that. But that left Erica un-monitored and she could do as she pleased, unnoticed.

"I keep throwing up," Erica told me in D.C.

"You probably just have a virus, and it'll pass."

"But I'm so tired."

Erica slept in my office when we went there for the day. In the small waiting room, she curled up on the gray couch and hours later woke up to go to the bathroom and then lay right back down. At my apartment she slept the whole time and was practically unable to help me pack.

"I haven't felt good for a few weeks."

She was nineteen. Her pediatrician had prescribed amoxicillin when she had seen her a few weeks earlier.

"Nicole, what's wrong with me? Why can't I keep anything down?"

"We'll go back to the doctor once we get home. You'll be fine," I told her.

I tried to call Gram daily and did so that night.

"Are you all packed up?" Gram asked.

"We are but Erica keeps sleeping and throwing up. I think she has the flu."

"Oh. How long has this been happening?" asked Gram.

"For a few weeks, I think. I made her some toast for dinner."

"Well, you girls be careful, ok?"

Gram didn't give anything away—that she maybe knew why Erica was sick.

As soon as we arrived home, Erica went to the ER. They asked her many questions. "Where have you been? How long have you been sick? Is there any chance you might be pregnant? Have you ever had sex?" When there was no other explanation available, they took an x-ray of her stomach looking for a bowel obstruction or something similar.

Linda had moved to rehab after her back surgery as she re-learned how to walk and take care of herself. She received more chemo and radiation. She wore a turtle shell from her waist up to her neck to protect her back while she healed. But she was improving, and she had finally stopped smoking.

Walt caught me before I went into Linda's room in the rehabilitation wing of the hospital and gave me a hug.

"Now don't be mad, but Erica's pregnant and your mother's fine with it."

"Erica's what? She's never had sex. What do you mean Linda's fine with it? This is horrible."

The fluorescent light streamed onto Walt's bald head, sweat beads forming as we spoke.

"Listen, you've got to get over it. It is what it is."

"How could she do this to us?"

"Calm down. There's nothing we can do now."

I was surprised that Linda was OK with everything. I wasn't. I imagined Erica's ruined life as a welfare mom, living off the state in a trailer.

I could see this because one of my best childhood friends had a baby at sixteen and wasn't able to finish high school. I attributed my friend's problems to the child.

I wanted a better life for my baby sister, so I immediately thought Erica should get an abortion.

"Erica, I don't want you to be a welfare mother. I want you to have a life. Having a kid now will ruin your life. Can't you understand that?"

"I'm keeping the baby," she said.

"You're too young."

"I'm not having an abortion."

"How are you going to pay for this child? Where are you going to live?"

"I'll work it out," she said.

"What about school?"

"Stop. I am keeping the baby," she yelled.

It never occurred to me that the responsibility for taking care of another human might lead a person to rise above, to do more with their life, to stretch themselves, to work a full-time job while attending community college. In this, I suffered a lack of imagination.

Because Linda recovered so quickly after she broke her back, she was able to move home. Before she came back from rehab, I had Linda's friends—a small army of energetic and committed women from church—come over and decontaminate her house, washing everything including the tar-stained walls and curtains. That way the house wouldn't smell like smoke, so Linda wouldn't want to start smoking again.

Sitting in the living room with me after she returned home, Linda said, "The only one of you guys I worry about is John. Dad was the hardest on him. He just continues to seek his Dad's approval."

"He'll be fine," I said.

"I sure hope so," said Linda.

John had wanted to stay home because Linda was sick. He wanted to take the semester off like I had done when Dad had been sick.

As a child, studies were never John's strong suit. Focusing on his homework challenged him and this led to lots of arguing. However, now he was excelling in North Dakota. He was even on the Dean's List.

Linda's biggest concern was that John was too much like Dad. He felt like the world was out to get him. He expected people to screw him. She was worried he would turn out just like his father.

"I don't want him coming back home," said Linda. "He needs to stay at school and finish. His grades are good and I want him to keep that momentum."

So I told John, "Stay at school and make Linda proud."

By then the doctors had changed her chemo to bi-weekly. We went to chemotherapy in a cold room. Fewer than a dozen recliners were in the room with piles of blankets around and TVs too. Movies, carefully chosen, played round the clock. No sad movies were shown, and there were lots of magazines: *People, Star, Glamour, Real Simple, Home and Garden, Reader's Digest*, and even a *Vogue* or two.

There were pictures just outside the room of the former patients, with thank you notes. Memorial notices were absent, but that made me feel like maybe this doctor's patients didn't die.

Linda rolled on in and said hello to the regulars. Then she settled into a few hours of chemicals coursing through her veins. I went with her a lot of the time, as did Walt. Erica and Montana stopped in sometimes too.

I read the *People* magazine to Linda and found the other patients perked up as I read. Like my first grade teacher, I held the magazine up and panned the room so others could see the dress I was describing or the people in the story I was reading. Linda commented. I commented.

"Did you see the dress she had on? The red looks horrible with her hair."

"Well, not as bad as you think. Did you see the pictures of Pierce Brosnan?"

Linda *loved* him.

Other people commented too, the lady with breast cancer or the man with a hole in his throat. We went through magazine after magazine like this, until Linda was too tired. Then I just watched Linda as she rested. When her eyes were closed, her mouth did this funny thing. It turned down, and her chin scrunched up a bit. I could see her purple eye shadow, from Japan. Linda said Japanese eyeshadow had the most pigment and thus was the most brilliant.

The old people there didn't scare Linda like they do some people.

There are people who don't know how to act around the elderly. Linda just chatted them up. She shouted so they could hear her. She sneaked them chocolate when they weren't supposed to have it. Every year Costco carried special holiday tins of cookies. She bought these to take to the retired nuns at our church. They loved the cookies and they loved her.

But she was vain. She cared about her appearance. She didn't like growing old herself. This wouldn't be a graceful process.

Years earlier I had chronicled, "Mom, when I'm thirty, you'll be sixty and Montana will be twenty. Can you imagine, when you are seventy, I'll be forty and Montana'll be thirty!"

Linda's face said she didn't want to keep talking about this.

Was it that she didn't want to think about getting older or that she didn't expect to?

The end of life from cancer is a slow ramping down of activities and abilities. I suppose this is also true of aging, but more visibly with cancer. When Linda realized she needed to take the hospital van to her doctor's appointments, did she realize she would never ride in her beloved Bronco again? Did she realize when we ordered the hospital bed for her to sleep in that she would never sleep in her own bed again? Did she quietly mourn the loss of these regularities? The last time she would be able to go to the bathroom by herself? Get a coffee? Empty the dishwasher? Have a glass of wine? Smoke a cigarette? Did she know she would never see her old self-reflected in the mirror?

Each of these things slipped slowly away, but fast enough that the unconcerned onlooker could see what was happening. Time went fast and slow.

A few weeks later Erica lay in bed exhausted again. Her bedroom was the size Linda's dressing room had been in our old house and her bed sat under one window, with mosquito netting hanging down and creating a princess-like feel.

"Why Erica? Why? Why did you do this to us?"

What started my tirade?

"Nicole, stop yelling at me."

"How could you go and get pregnant in the middle of all of this?"

I just snapped. My mind was racing. I could no longer handle the situation: estranged father, fighting parents, dying mother, and pregnant sister. I went downstairs and poured water on Erica's work pants in the dryer.

"Why did you do that, Nicole? I needed to rest. And now I will be late for work. I don't have any other clothes. Can't you help me, please?"

Erica's blue eyes pleaded with me, but I felt vindicated. I had shown her how I felt.

What had I shown her? That I was crazy and mean? Unreliable? Who had I shown this to? Carol, Linda's best friend, who was visiting us from Maryland? Or Linda, in the living room lying in her bed, worrying about her little urchins and how they would make do without her?

Linda had a real reason to worry about us. And me.

Erica must have been terrified. Her mother was dying. Dad offered to "adopt" her child, to give it a better life. Dad's insurance didn't cover pregnancy for dependents. Even if it had, she would have soon lost coverage because of her age. On top of everything, her older sister was a raving lunatic about her pregnancy. Erica had planned on going away to college, however, that was up in the air now. Even before Linda became sick, Erica was unsure about where to study and how to pay for it. And her boyfriend, now seen with clearer eyes, was wholly unreliable. Her only clear ally, with a chance of helping her through it, was Walt. He championed Erica and supported her.

Other people were also supportive of Erica's choice. She saw a doctor who went to our church. He lived his convictions. Erica was on Medicaid by this point, which wouldn't cover his fees, so he saw Erica for free. He didn't believe in abortion.

After I lost my shit, screaming at Erica, I decided it was a good idea for the whole family to start seeing Dr. T. I, we, had more to deal with than we could handle.

"Guys, I called and made an appointment for us with Dr. T. We need help."

We met with him weekly while Linda was sick and sometimes called him for "emergency sessions." His receptionist would schedule us after his regular patients. He knew the whole story with Linda and Dad, which helped him help us.

Linda's modest house had a kitchen that opened into the dining room and behind a small wall was the living room, filled with furniture made for a much larger room. We reconfigured the living room to accommodate Linda's hospital bed. In front of the bed, on the entrance hall table sat the TV with the couches arranged around it. She slept there. Walt slept on one of the couches. The other couch sat parallel to her bed. Between the bed and the couch was a side table that held medical supplies such as cold cloths, water glasses, Ensure for Linda's stomach tube, pain drugs, and a blue bean-shaped tray from the hospital for her when she threw up.

One morning I stood in Linda's kitchen in a gray onesie. As a child, I always wore onesies to bed. I loved them. When I saw one that was for adults, I was excited. I ordered it for Gram because I thought it was a cute gift. But she didn't want an adult onesie, so I started wearing it, and wearing it, without a bra. I wore nothing else without a bra. In fact, the only nightmares about high school I ever had were of me forgetting my bra and calling Linda to bring me one. She told me I had to figure it out in the dream.

In my onesie, I felt cozy and warm.

"Nicole!?" Linda said with urgency.

I ran into the living room.

"The tray, the tray."

Linda didn't ever throw up. Before she had cancer, that is.

As a child, I had called out to Linda, on my knees in the bathroom, throwing up because of the stomach flu, "Mom, come help me, please. I'm sick."

As I looked up from the toilet, she stood in the door with this horrible look on her face. Her chin scrunched up somehow and her eyes kind of squinted.

"You should pull your hair back. Here's a cold cloth. Call me when you are done."

"But, Mom I need you."

"No, you don't. You're throwing up."

A stainless steel metal bowl in case of more throwing up was left by my bed.

Now I grabbed a washcloth while Linda threw up into the small blue bean tray. Who designed these dumb blue trays? They were so small. Who, in the history of the world, only daintily throws up? No one. These trays needed to be bigger. I needed to have multiple blue bean trays for them to be of any help. At the end of the day, the trays were more of a talisman against throwing up. If one was around, my likelihood of needing it decreased, but not that day.

As I was wetting a washcloth for Linda in the bathroom, Erica came in.

"I don't feel good," she said.

"You haven't felt good."

Suddenly Erica was getting sick in the toilet.

From the basement, I heard Montana's small voice, "Nicole?!"

He had just had surgery for a broken leg suffered on an ill-fated church ski trip. I rushed down the stairs, still holding the cool cloth for Linda.

"What, Montana?"

"I don't feel good."

Shit. He was throwing up too. At least Walt remained healthy.

2000, Montana

I had believed Linda was healing while she was in rehab and now things were looking even better. The tumor on her neck was smaller. The radiation was helping. Everything was going to go back to normal. I was broke and I hated borrowing money from my sick mom.

"I'm going back to work."

"Ok. I don't want you to lose your job. They've been so generous letting you come out here for so long," said Linda.

"Is it ok?"

"Walt's here. Go, keep your job."

The day before I left I saw our dentist at the gym.

"How's Linda?"

"She's great. She's back home and improving."

"What kind of cancer does she have?" he asked.

"They still don't know, but she's responding well to the chemo."

The dentist looked at me with pity. I could see it in his eyes. He understood what was happening.

Grandparents and toddlers are often accused of having selective hearing. People sometimes have selective understanding. When your brain just can't process some piece of information, it just chooses to ignore it. That was where I was with Linda's cancer—unable to process that Linda would soon no longer exist in the world. I didn't see it coming.

So, I drove off. I left. Between Montana and D.C.—five days on the road—I didn't call home once.

"Nicole, where have you been? We were worried about you. I missed you," said Linda when finally I did call.

That horrible feeling in the pit of my stomach bubbled up. I knew I should have been calling, but I pretended everything was fine, and I didn't need to call Linda every day to see how she was.

"I'm sorry, Lin."

I'd abandoned her. I didn't want to face that. I wanted Linda to be well. I knew I would desperately miss her and I was subconsciously testing out how it felt to not be able to call her whenever I wanted to.

Choosing not to call for a few days versus not ever being able to ever call her again, these were two entirely different things.

"Erica had her baby shower, and it went off without a hitch," said Linda. I had missed Erica's shower.

Linda's friends helped her plan it and were the main people in attendance. The women knew the shower was taking place a bit early because Linda probably wouldn't live to see the baby born, not that anyone said that out loud.

"I think Erica has everything she needs for the baby, now. Baby blankets and clothes and diapers," said Linda.

I cringed. I didn't like people planning for Linda to be dead. That's what Linda was implying. Erica had the stuff she needed for the baby since Linda wouldn't be there.

But Linda wasn't dying. Why didn't anyone else think that too? Couldn't they see that acting like Linda was dying just made it more likely?

I had missed Erica's shower on purpose because I was still angry with her for the pregnancy.

After a few weeks in D.C., I realized I couldn't stay. I was lying to myself about Linda recovering. Linda knew this too. She understood. I wanted everyone to be wrong. I wanted another miracle. I wanted her to meet Erica's baby. I wanted her and Walt to get to drive an RV around the US. She and Gram still weren't speaking. I wanted them to reconcile. I wanted Linda to see me get married. I wanted to take Linda to the Great Wall of China and Australia. I wanted to go back to the hot springs we had passed up in Canada.

John kept going to school. Erica's tummy kept growing larger. Montana went to school. Walt took care of Linda. We were barely able to function.

I have a theory that people only die when their work on Earth is done, whatever that work is. Linda's work had been raising John, Erica, Montana, and I to be kind, productive members of society. Montana was only fourteen, but she could tell he would make it. Her work here was done.

Again, more magical thinking. There were many other things Linda could have done. Her work wasn't done. She hadn't played with grandchildren or seen Montana graduate from high school. The theory fails.

As much as I repeated the mantra, "We're all alive or we're all dying," it didn't change the reality. Even if we know we will die at some point, not all of us have such a "date certain" for our end.

I went back.

Once I came home again, Walt, Linda, and I watched *Who Wants to Be a Millionaire* every night. Walt knew every answer to the questions in the game show. Watching with him was both amazing and annoying.

"Who is the inventor of the Showtime Rotisserie?"

Four answers came up. One of the options was Ron Popeil. Walt chose him, correctly. Popeil invited a number of excellent "as seen on TV" kitchen devices like the Chop-O-Matic and rotisserie for making roast chicken at home on the countertop.

"You know, I dated him," said Linda casually from her hospital bed.

"What?" asked Walt and I in unison.

"I dated him. He was a nice guy and now he's super rich. I chose the wrong guy."

"You dated Ron Popeil? Wow. I had no idea," I said.

The game show went on but we sat there in baffled silence. Ron Popeil could have been my dad! Linda was contemplating what life would have held with him, and we were all wondering if we would have ended up in the same place. Linda sick with Walt and me taking care of her.

After the show, Linda brushed her teeth in bed. Walt got Linda a glass of water and her pills. The pain pills were important. Bone cancer is well known to be almost intolerably painful and by this point, she was in near constant pain. She had long-acting pain pills and then ones that were for acute pain.

The doctors had told us to stay ahead of the pain. Take pain pills before you start having pain, but not too early so as to run out of the pain pills before the prescription allows you to pick up more. Linda didn't like how the pain medication made her feel so she was always reluctant to take them.

The house had turned into a pharmacy. Medicine bottles lined the kitchen counter. We had a system for making sure that the pills we needed were nearby, but that system wasn't readily apparent to visitors. Walt picked up the pills at Shopko, a local mega-mart chain. The pharmacist knew him. He kindly asked how Linda felt, but he could tell based on the drugs Walt was picking up.

When we ran out of a pain medication, he called around to the other pharmacies until he found the drug she needed. This was important because Linda couldn't tolerate every drug. Sometimes she needed the generic instead of the brand name version and sometimes she needed two pills instead of one big pill. Thank goodness this pharmacist was happy to get Linda the pills that worked. Little things like this had an outsized impact on our lives.

One of the medicines that worked well was Thalidomide of "thalidomide babies" notoriety. In the 60's the drug had been used to help women with morning sickness. However, it became quickly evident that the drug caused deformities in the babies of these women. Before giving it to Linda, the doctors had her sign repeatedly saying that the fifty-six-year-old with a broken back wasn't pregnant, having sex, nor planning on becoming pregnant, or having any more sex so as to become pregnant. The drug worked like magic and immediately calmed her stomach.

After watching TV, I retired to Linda's room on the other side of the wall from the living room. I often read a whole book a night. My reading varied, but almost all were novels and reliably an Oprah pick. The books I read I normally wouldn't have thought of picking up. Too commercial? Too something. I stayed up too late reading every night. Two a.m., I should go to bed, I would think. Just a few more pages. Three a.m. Go to bed. Four a.m. *Now.* Sleep. I reluctantly put the book away and slept.

Once, in the middle of the night, after I was done reading the rare nonfiction book, *Tuesdays with Morrie*, I started to more consciously understand that Linda might die. She might not be miraculously saved as Dad had been. Morrie died at the end of the book. I cried and couldn't stop hyperventilating.

I sat there in Linda's bed, just feet from Linda and Walt sleeping in the living room. I was having a meltdown. I imagined life without Linda, my mom. How would it feel? Horrible. How could I ever live without her? I couldn't. I wouldn't have Dad to lean on. It would just be me and the kids and Walt. I would need to set a good example for the kids then.

But still, I held on to the thought that she could heal, that the cancer could go away. Thinking this allowed me to calm down and sleep. Dad had recovered, so would my mother.

At eight a.m. I rolled out of bed and tried to wake up Montana. By then Walt had already tried a few times. Then I drove Montana to school in the gray onesie, messy hair and all. God help me if we were in an accident. I did always wear a bra when driving, so at least that was one thing.

Back at the house, I ate breakfast instead of showering and grabbed the computer and sat down with Linda.

We were shopping on the internet for buttons. She normally found them at the Salvation Army. She was always looking for special glass buttons that were round and had images inside of the glass. The button encyclopedia sat nearby for ready reference. We tried to outbid others on eBay but lost often.

While she slept, I practiced calligraphy at our kitchen table. Hours and hours of a, a, a, a, a, b, b, b, b, over and over. If Linda didn't have a doctor's appointment, I might do the laundry, go shopping for food, or go to the gym. While Dad had been sick, I'd learned the importance of exercising when in a crisis. I also applied to law school.

"Mom, I just don't know if I should go to law school." I had planned to go to law school before cancer interfered.

"Well, it's expensive," said Linda.

Law school *was* expensive. And every time I contemplated law school, this was my first thought, "Would the experience justify the cost?" I was admitted to the three law schools I applied to, but once it was clear that Linda needed me more than I needed to go to law school, I deferred my admittance. I still wasn't sure if I would go, but I didn't need to decide for another year.

I tried to get Linda to visualize healing. One of Linda's friends who had survived breast cancer gave us some books about the power of thought in healing. I had Linda draw pictures of her body killing the cancer cells like a child would do as instructed by the book.

Linda slept a lot. People do that when they're sick. In retrospect, this was the first sign of her cancer. She had slept through our whole trip to Canada.

With yet another new chemo, her hair began falling out. This was no big surprise. Every "made-for-TV" movie about cancer has a scene where the woman's hair falls out. But Linda's hair mattered because it was all that remained.

Watching it fall out in clumps proved too much, and her roots were all gray. Better to just get rid of it. Linda's friend and hairdresser Joyce came over and shaved her head. For more than a decade they had seen each other once a month for four hours at a pop. She helped Linda find a cute wig. Instead of a bob, like Linda often had, the wig had a short yet stylish cut. Modern, save the fact that it was a wig. The wig made Linda's scalp itch but allowed her to look and feel better.

Even after Linda didn't have hair, Linda's hairdresser came every week to see Linda. She just hung out with us. She pitched in. She helped give Linda a bath or with some other indignity without batting an eye. She acted normal, which is just what Linda needed.

In addition to her hairdresser coming over, another woman just started showing up at our house. She was short and a little round. She was nice, though. She just came right in and cleaned everything. The kitchen had become a general disaster. We weren't good at emptying the dishwasher, which led to a backup of dishes in the sink. Linda had always emptied it with coffee and a cigarette. We were five people living together who hadn't done so in years. Instead of a family's home, it sometimes seemed more like a group house with people coming and going at different times of the day.

This woman cooked too. She brought food over. Her son had gone to Catholic school with Montana, but she wasn't in Linda's normal group of friends from church. And, she lived way out of town in the valley. When she wasn't there, we talked about her. We speculated about why she was coming over? Why did she want to do our dishes? Perhaps she was lonely because her husband worked in Alaska on oil rigs.

While we looked forward to seeing Linda's hairdresser, we had an odd lack of feeling about this other woman. I wouldn't have recognized her if I ran into her at the grocery.

The woman was there in our house five out of seven days a week for months and then gone. She was there until she wasn't, and then we had to figure out how to do the dishes ourselves.

On Friday nights we put Linda in her wheelchair and walked over to the restaurant that was closest to our house. Linda enjoyed the fresh air. She had on her blond wig and wore her favorite lipstick. Linda tried to smile as we rolled her to dinner. We had to be careful traversing bumps in the sidewalk going there because the bumps hurt Linda's back.

The restaurant was in our town's former pizza joint with booths and an old salad bar covered up. We could roll her right up to the table. They served American Bistro food. I had the head of roasted garlic with bread every time I went. I then smelled like a giant roasted head of garlic for the next few days.

In the spring air, rolling home with Linda, there was a sense of hope in the family. Things were fine. They were going to be fine.

Linda's cancer had finally been named: Squamous Cell Carcinoma of

Unknown Primary. She was back at the hospital for her monthly whole body MRI scan to check for more cancer. The orderlies were dressed in white and with a kind of glassy-eyed look they were transferring her from her bed to a gurney. I watched everything intently searching Linda's face for signs of pain. I didn't want to micromanage the transfer, but anytime she was moved, it might break her back. She was delicate.

I saw her grimace and start groaning. She scrunched up her chin and grabbed the side of the hospital bed, her knuckles turning white.

"Slow down. Can't you see she's in pain?"

No response. They didn't seem to hear me. Linda kept her grip strong. The kept moving at the same pace.

A bit louder, "You need to understand that you can break her back. You need to carefully lift up the sheet below her to move her."

Again, no response from these stoners. Linda's face was becoming more and more contorted.

"Ouch!" screamed Linda.

Linda never mentioned the pain.

"Stop! You are hurting her. Why aren't you listening to me?" I screamed.

I finally had their attention.

I couldn't understand why these people hadn't reacted to Linda. I had to scream in the hospital. Then they looked up at me in disbelief.

"Either you go slower and do this nicely or I am ordering you to stop. You're hurting my mother."

Still no response, but they did take notice of her finally and slowly completed the transfer from bed to gurney. Off she went for the test.

I think it was the environment. There was so much suffering in hospitals that the people who worked there became acclimated or immune to the suffering. It's how they made it through the day. I needed to be there to advocate for Linda. Otherwise, she wouldn't receive the best level of care the institution could offer.

The time between the scan and the doctors giving us the results was the most difficult. Was there more cancer? Was the chemo working? Cancer doesn't generally make people sick, but the effect of the rapidly growing cells in the wrong places does. Eventually, these cells take up too much space, displacing the bones and breaking something. Or they take over an organ, so it can no longer perform its function.

Days later, Walt, Linda, and I sat around our butcher-block table in the kitchen. The back surgeon called to tell us the results of her MRI. That he was even willing to talk to us on the phone about the results seemed strange. Normally, we had to come into the office for the test results. He spoke to each of us in turn, with a kind voice, telling us the same thing.

"Nicole, I'm sorry to tell you this, but her spine has cancer up and down it. She needs to stay in bed to ensure that her back doesn't break again. We wouldn't be able to fix it a second time."

We hung up the phone and stared at each other. Linda had her massive back brace on.

Linda asked, "Who's going out to get me a carton of cigarettes?"

Walt and I slowly turned to look at her.

"I'm just kidding. Let's get me back into bed."

As the days rolled by, Linda and I were together a lot and Linda wanted to talk about Dad much of the time.

One summer day, as I scrolled through buttons at eBay she prattled on.

"Why did he leave me for her? What does she have that I don't have?"

"Mom, let it go. Do you like this globe button? It has a rose in it."

"Yes, it's nice. But what does he see in her?"

"I don't know."

"Well, do you like her? You don't like her, do you?"

Erica walked in.

"Erica, could you do your imitation of Dad's wife?" Linda asked.

Erica's tummy was big and growing. She was having a boy.

With a fake Asian accent, "Jack, what can I get you?" Erica put her arms up at her side, wrists limp, and she stooped over, taking little steps, as though her feet were bound.

"Jack, what do you want? What do you want? Can I lotion your feet? Do your laundry? Wipe your butt?"

Linda laughed. I laughed. Erica laughed. It was totally inappropriate and racist.

"Jack, what else can I do for you? What do you need?" Erica continued.

She did capture my Dad's wife and how solicitous she was of him. Linda and Dad had never been like this with one another. Theirs had been an equal partnership, at least as it related to communication between each other. Dad needed to put his own dishes in the dishwasher, just like the rest of us. While we laughed, I felt uncomfortable because of Erica's politically incorrect portrayal of Dad's wife. But in that moment we showed complete solidarity with Linda. Through making fun of the other, we solidified our own group.

As we talked—or rather she ranted—I learned lots of other details about my parents' relationship.

"Married for twenty-five years and he just drops me. Who was there for him when he was sick? Who took care of his children? Who kept this family together?"

Sometimes, Linda sounded a little crazed.

I didn't talk to Dad while Linda was sick, even though we were both often in the same town. Dad lived some of the time in Lakeside, Montana, twenty minutes south of Kalispell, and some of the time in Vancouver, Washington. His wife hadn't yet retired from flying. I hadn't spoken to him since he had cut me off financially. Every time I tried, he made me mad, pumping me for information about Linda or the kids, or asking me for money, ironically.

But I saw him sometimes when he drove over to pick up Montana for the weekend. He rolled up in a purple Mercedes. Dad was colorblind. He couldn't tell the difference between purple and blue. This hadn't stopped him from becoming a pilot or buying purple cars he thought were blue.

"Now, Dad says he doesn't have any money. Well, then, how is he driving a Mercedes? He never bought me a Mercedes. He says his wife bought it. Right, on a flight attendant's salary," Linda ranted.

When I saw him, I felt apprehensive and sad. I wanted him to miss me.

Had I known that he would never give in, I might have capitulated. I might have given him what he wanted, money, control. Instead, I just tried to ignore the situation, assuming that time would eventually change things.

"All those years and he tried to screw me out of everything and turn you kids against me. Well, I showed him, didn't I? I have a life. I have a house. I have friends. And, I have you guys. Who do you call first? Me or your father?"

Linda was getting exercised.

"I know how to keep my children. I have spent my whole life helping my urchins grow."

"Mom, we love you. Everything's fine."

"What your father did is not acceptable."

During the next few weeks, Linda continued with chemo even while bedridden, but once she was bedridden, she couldn't keep seeing Dr. T and really she didn't need to see him anymore. She had a kind of grace about everything. She stopped droning on and on about Dad. The kids, Walt, and I needed him, though. So we kept seeing him.

2000, Montana

SINCE Linda couldn't leave the house anymore, people came to her. Every Friday night her girlfriends from church came over for a little party. I ran to the wine store and picked up a few bottles of sweet Moscato wine before everyone arrived.

We sat around and retold funny family stories, like the time years earlier when Dad had forgotten Montana at the store.

Don't all parents forget their children in stores sometimes?

No.

Oh. Interesting.

That day, Jenny and I had just gotten out of the hot tub in the old house. Linda kept yelling for Montana to come and get lunch. We sat down to a sandwich in our swimming suits. Uncle Frankie, Dad's brother, was there too.

"Frankie, have you seen Montana?" Linda asked.

"No."

"Jack, have you seen Montana?" she asked.

Just then the look of recognition ran across Dad's face. A millisecond later he was headed towards the front door yelling, "Call the hardware store."

Unfortunately, even in our small town, there was more than one hardware store.

Dad found Montana crying hysterically. Dad told Montana he could get any toy that he wanted. Montana chose a John Deere combine.

We laughed at the story, emblematic of all of Dad's transgressions.

At these parties, everyone treated Linda normally, and Linda was buoyed by these weekly get-togethers. She'd known these women for years. They were mostly younger than she, but a few were her age. Mary had three girls, one of whom was Montana's age. Karen had survived breast cancer and could see the situation clearly. She also hated that I called my mom Linda. "She's your mother for goodness sake. Call her Mom." Teri fostered newborns before they were adopted. There were others too, a changing cast of characters, friends.

They went on to compare the new-new priest to the old-new priest, who took the place of our old priest who had died of complications from a liver transplant. The old-new priest was the one who told Linda and Dad to get divorced. The new-new priest, Father Kevin, was there for Linda's emergency back surgery. He understood our congregation.

"Father Kevin could be the Pope. He's just that good," said Linda.

These women were important because Linda had had a difficult time making friends in town when we moved to Montana. People found Linda to be strange, overly direct, verging on bawdy, different. She wore makeup and never wore boots. She hated blue jeans. It took her years to find her group. They could reminisce about the school fundraisers where Linda tap-danced in a tutu, or the old-new priest telling the choir they didn't know how to sing.

These Friday nights gave Linda something to look forward to. They reminded her that she had friends who not only cared about her but who also could hang out with her and act like nothing was wrong. They could treat her normally and not ask, "*How* are you?" When other people asked that question, they were really asking, "*Are* you dying soon?"

A few days later, she and I were shopping, online, and talking. I sat next to her hospital bed.

"Nicole, I don't want a grave." This came out of nowhere.

"I don't want you and the kids and Walt to have someplace to go to be sad. I don't want it. I want to be cremated. You need to move on after I am gone."

"What do you think about this button?"

I pointed at the screen.

"It will be better for you if you don't have a place to go to be sad when I'm gone. And pick the cheapest option for everything. I'll be dead. Don't waste money on that stuff."

I wanted to move this conversation on. I wasn't prepared to talk to Linda about life after she was dead.

"Ok," was all I could muster.

"Sprinkle me in Glacier Park."

I changed the subject to Gram. I had expected with time that they would reconcile.

"Come on. Can't you forgive her? What's the big deal?" I asked while we scrolled through yet more button listings on eBay.

"I don't want to see or talk to her again."

"But she's your mom, and you're sick. She wants to help."

"I need some pain medication. It's starting to hurt," said Linda.

"Mom, come on," I replied.

She was changing the subject now.

"Please?" I asked.

"The meds, Nicole."

Apparently, none of them—Linda, Dad, Gram, Mr. Miserable—could sit down and work out their problems. Instead, people cut each other off permanently. Relationship over.

Talking about the problem would have meant one side would have needed to admit fault in the altercation.

I can't easily cut people off, but sometimes people have indeed needed to be extricated from my life. I get it. I just don't want to be the extricated *or* do the extricating. The neon blinking outlier was Dad. What had I done to him? I don't know what to say.

One of the books I read in the middle of the night while Linda was sick was Suze Orman's personal finance book. Linda had purchased it at Costco before she became sick. The book gave basic no-nonsense financial advice.

At this point, Linda was financially secure. She'd received her divorce settlement, bought a house, and invested the rest in mutual funds. She received child support when Dad paid it for Montana. Unfortunately, twenty-five years of habitually never having any money meant she was loath to spend it when she finally had it.

"Linda, Suze says that the only way to ensure that Montana gets his money and Dad doesn't take it is to set up a trust so that the money is tied up until Montana is eighteen. That way he'll be an adult and able to make his own decisions. Until then, you can set up the trust to give out a monthly allotment of money to each of us and pay the mortgage."

Montana would be fifteen in a few months.

The trust would ensure that Linda's wishes were followed. People make fun of Suze, but she helped our family.

After an attorney set up the trust, we needed to make a list of who Linda wanted her physical belongings to go to.

One day Linda and I, instead of internet shopping, sat down to write out the list.

"We have to do this," I said.

"Where do we start?"

We were using a yellow legal pad to write everything out.

"First, write down, 'NO FIGHTING,'" she said.

Linda constantly told us not to fight. We didn't fight as much anymore, but we could always use the reminder.

"I want you to have the green vanity in my bedroom, the one I repainted. John gets the baker's cabinet that Walt and I stripped and repainted," said Linda. "Erica gets my secretary. Montana is to get the tea cart from Neiman's." The cart was chrome with two shelves and inlaid glass made of what looked like thinly sliced conch shells with an iridescent quality. Linda always kept our liquor on the cart, even though no one in our family, save Walt, drank liquor.

"What else?"

"What about the ring?"

As a child, I had asked Linda to let me try on her engagement ring with three large diamonds. She never let me. She only took it off if she was cleaning it. Otherwise, the ring was on her finger. Dad had given her a solitaire when they were married and then two more diamonds as children appeared.

"You get the biggest diamond, then John gets the next largest one, and Erica gets the smallest. Montana gets the eternity band."

"But that's not fair. The big one's worth more," I said.

"It's not fair, but they're diamonds. I can't change their size. This is how I want it done."

Things were getting a little heavy for me. I tried to ignore that the items delineated an action to take place after Linda died. I looked around the room. The sun fell through the bay window. Summer was happening outside. Erica spent some of her spare time tending Linda's garden with sweet peas and wildflowers from seed packets. We sat inside making the list.

"What about the silver?"

"Divide that up among the four of you."

"But that doesn't make sense. Everyone having a bit of silver."

We had a silverware set and amazing silver goblets with a mid-century look. She'd received these as wedding gifts.

"I don't have any other ideas."

Linda was getting tired.

"Every kid gets their own car. The boys can have the guns. Give Montana the serger."

"But Montana doesn't even know how to sew. He can have the sewing machine. I'll take the serger."

She agreed.

"Well, how about *The War* picture?"

When Linda's brother was a struggling art student, she had purchased *The War* picture from him. The word "WAR" was the center of the drawing and around it in charcoal and graphite were different images he had drawn of war. Previously, the picture always hung in our basement, but it was now hanging in Montana's bedroom. He liked the image, as did I.

"That's Montana's."

"But I always wanted that picture," I said.

"Then you'll have to have Montana make a copy for you."

I heard myself sounding like the entitled brat I could be. I was bickering with my dying mother about a silly piece of art, but sometimes it's easier to focus on the details, the logistics, rather than face life.

I broke down crying. I didn't want to even contemplate this topic anymore.

"I don't want any of these things. I want you. I don't want you to die."

"Let's finish this later."

So I put the yellow legal pad on the kitchen table where it stayed. The list of who was to get her belongings that she cared about when she died should have been signed and dated, adding to its authenticity. Without the signatures, it looked like a list I had written by myself.

2000, Montana

WE kept a log of Linda's temperature, her medications, and any other important notes by the telephone. Taking her temperature was more difficult than it should have been. As soon as anyone noted that Linda was feeling different we grabbed the thermometer.

"It says her temp is 96.5."

"Well, take it again."

"Do you feel warm, Mom?" I asked.

"No, not really."

"What does it say now?"

"101.4."

This happened over and over until someone hit upon the idea that the thermometer might be bad. Such was our combined confusion and lack of ability to think clearly about the problem facing us. Walt went back and forth to the store because we kept getting defective thermometers. The under-the-tongue thermometers were apparently notoriously inaccurate. No one ever mentioned this at the store. Three trips later, an in-ear thermometer for substantially more money was purchased from Costco. If it didn't work we could at least return it.

Walt and I made sure that everything was written in the log. Her pain levels, when she took her pills, and we even noted when she pooped. Pooping took on new importance. We could tell if her body was working properly if she was pooping regularly.

Hospice was mentioned around the edges. People tried to bring it up, but hospice would have telegraphed to Linda to give up. I wanted her to fight. Giving up wasn't an option.

I had a superstitious aversion to speaking audibly about Linda possibly dying, almost as if merely bringing such an idea out into the world by speaking it aloud might make it happen sooner. Her death had been spoken of, however. The doctor had told us at the beginning and others had tried to bring it up.

That wasn't what hospice was about, but that was how it made me feel at the time. I couldn't react rationally to Linda dying. In keeping with a long modeled pattern, I ignored the fact that she might be more comfortable in hospice. What I did do was try to keep our normal life rolling along, maintaining that this was merely a crisis that we would emerge from intact.

I called the doctor's office, something I seemed to do more and more often.

"Hi, yes, this is Nicole Harkin, Linda Harkin's daughter. She hasn't pooped in five days." Again, the realities of pooping were explained to me. "Yes, I know normal is anywhere from six poops in one day to one poop every six days." I disliked talking about poop. "Yes, she's bedridden. What should we do?" He repeated more of what I knew. "We've tried Senna." Senna's a stool softener. "And fiber. Yes." I covered the phone and turned to Linda. "Mom, they think you have to go to the hospital if you are in pain. What do you want to do?"

We both looked at Walt.

"The doctor thinks you may have a bowel obstruction and he wants you to go to the hospital."

Because I didn't like to talk about poop, I didn't ask enough questions of the doctor when he was on the phone. Namely, what can you do for Linda if she does have a bowel obstruction?

Just before we headed to the hospital, Erica said, "Nicole, I can't get the dryer to turn on."

"What Erica? We need to go."

"My pants are wet."

She was seven months pregnant at this point and not many clothes were fitting. Walt went to look at it while I dealt with the ambulance.

"I think it's dead," he said.

The dryer was ten years old, not that old, but having it fixed never crossed my mind. Our house couldn't function without a dryer. Five people were living in the house and a broken dryer seemed catastrophic. We needed a new dryer quickly.

She did, in fact, have a bowel obstruction, but surgery to fix it wasn't recommended by the doctor because she could bleed to death.

After Linda was in the hospital for a day I called the doctor to find out how she was going to be fixed. I was in Linda's Bronco, the Bronco she had purchased because "I look good in it." The windows were down. I had heard a story earlier that morning on NPR about how important autopsies are for science. People weren't requesting them or allowing them anymore and without this data, science suffered.

I explained who I was.

"Yes, the doctor is working on your mother's case."

"Right, but when? When can I see him? When can I talk to him?"

"He's busy right now, but I can have him call you?"

Through sobs, "Please, my mom needs help. Let me talk to him."

She tried one more time, but I pressed and cried even more. She finally put the doctor on the phone.

"What are you doing to help her?" I asked.

"There's nothing we can do," he said.

"What do you mean? You have to help her."

"Your mother's dying."

Until then, no one had said that to me in a manner in which I could hear it.

I sat in the parking lot sobbing. And then I called people. I called Gram and told her to come out. I called my aunt and uncle. I called her estranged father, Mr. Miserable. I called her friends. I sent up an alarm to rally the troops.

Then I realized that I needed to buy a new dryer before Linda died. After Linda died we wouldn't have access to her money for some time. A dryer cost more than Erica, on her movie theater manager's income or I, not working, could afford. Linda would have wanted us to have a dryer. Well, she would have understood. I couldn't ask her because she was slipping in and out of consciousness by this point. Discussing dead dryers seemed too mundane.

The dryer drama served as a distraction. I could obsess about the dryer rather than grieving the impending loss of Linda. I had a reason to leave the hospital. I had something that needed to be done before the end.

I drove to the appliance store in a small strip mall. I looked at the row of dryers. Someone came up to help me. I wasn't in the mood to discuss the dryers in depth. I had her power of attorney and signed one of her checks to buy a dryer. They delivered the dryer the next day. I felt dumb worrying about the dryer when Linda was in the hospital dying.

I heard these lines in my head, "We're either alive or dead. Otherwise, we are all waiting to die, dying."

I didn't want to wait for Linda to die. I wanted her to live, so I acted as if she weren't dying.

Linda was in a small hospital room with institutional lighting. Many of her friends were there, coming in and out of the room. Father Kevin was called and came by. We laughed and talked. We crowded around her bed.

This period of time in the hospital allowed me to process, transition even, into the reality that Linda was dying. I shifted away from denial.

People told her it was "ok for her to die."

That was what I was supposed to say, but it wasn't OK. I said it but didn't believe it. It wasn't OK that she was leaving us, but she was, and I needed to deal with that.

When it became clear to the hospital that Linda wasn't going home and would have lots of visitors, they moved her—us— into another room. This new room was much bigger and better appointed with a view of the mountains. She had a morphine drip that cut the pain but also put her to sleep. Too much morphine will put a person to sleep permanently. To skirt euthanasia laws, patients are given morphine and it hastens their death. This was what was happening, even though no one said it out loud as such. And she had so much pain.

Even with the morphine, which she was supposed to somehow control while being high and out of it, she was in pain. But she still wanted to participate, to live. The new, bigger room had everyone standing on the other side of the room, trying to escape death.

"Nicole, ask everyone to stand over here so I can hear them," Linda asked in a moment of clarity, her voice pleading.

I ushered everyone back over to her side of the room, but people naturally drifted away.

Gram flew out to Montana.

"Mom, Gram's here to see you."

"I don't want to ever see her again."

This had to be the haze of her illness. She was dying. Of course, she wanted to see her mom.

"But, Mom, please."

"Nicole, I've already told you. I don't want to see her."

Once Linda could no longer refuse to see her, Gram went to the hospital. Gram held her hand and talked to her. Who was I to keep Gram from Linda?

Her friends Mary and Teri stood over her.

"Remember when they went on that great European vacation?" Mary asked Teri, sounding slightly Minnesotan.

"Where did they go?" asked Teri.

"You know, I don't remember," said Mary.

"Legoland," said Linda.

She hadn't spoken for a day. She was still in there. She was still listening. That's the last thing she said. Legoland. It had been our best family trip.

Mr. Miserable sent a large bouquet of flowers. Someone put them on a table across the room from Linda. Her kidneys stopped producing urine, so she became more and more puffy, so much so that she couldn't even open her eyes. I tried to describe what the flower arrangement from her father looked like since she couldn't see them. She hadn't spoken to him in more than twenty years, and now she was too sick to talk to him.

We kissed her one by one and put a little cross on her forehead before we left that night to go home.

"We'll see you in the morning, Mom."

"We love you."

Walt stayed the night with her.

For so many things in life, you don't know you are doing something for the last time until after you've done it. You can't take in the moment and fully engage with it. Only later do you realize that it had been the last time.

2000, Montana

THE call came into Linda's house around ten that morning while we slept. I jumped up and answered the phone. I had gone from being a deep sleeper to someone who could be wide-awake in a nanosecond.

On the other end of the line, the nurse said, "You need to get to the hospital as soon as you can."

"What? Why? What's wrong?"

"Please just come to the hospital with your family as soon as possible."

I ran through the house yelling to John, Erica, and Montana to wake up. I hoped that the urgency in my voice would make them move. They dressed quickly. I then drove to pick up Gram who was staying at her friend's house.

I tried not to contemplate why the nurse had called us that way. I didn't want to think about what was happening. I kept my mind on my immediate task: get to the hospital. As we drove to the hospital, it began raining. For days we had waited for her to die. She was no longer responsive in the hospital. She just lay there.

She was dead when we arrived. She was gone. She had been dead when the nurse called us. The date was June 17th.

Teri said, "I had just told Walt to go home and shower. He didn't want to leave, but I told him he would feel better after a shower. Almost as soon as he was gone, she stopped breathing. It was like she was waiting for none of you guys to be here. I shook her, 'Linda, Linda wake up.' I called to the nurse's station. 'She's not breathing.' Everyone came running in, but she was gone."

I counted in my head. Linda has been dead for one hour. Then tomorrow she will have been dead for one day. Then one week. Then one month. Then a year. In ten years Linda will have been dead for a decade. How would ten years be without Linda? How soon would I start forgetting her voice or her face? Would I still be able to hear her sayings in my head? My brain spiraled outward. How would I be able to go on? I was twenty-four and my mom was dead. Montana was only fourteen. Erica was nineteen and seven months pregnant. John was only twenty-one.

I physically collapsed next to her hospital bed but didn't cry. I couldn't believe she was gone. A little more than six months after that call from Walt, it was over. She looked so peaceful there, dead. Can you have peace if you are dead, I wondered. No, I thought, you're just dead. Alive people can be peaceful. Dead people are empty bodies.

The hospital let us stay in the room for a bit. We stood over her puffy body. Her hair was short and gray. Her nails weren't painted red. That's what it was then. Just a body.

I requested an autopsy and that her organs be donated. Her corneas were the only body parts they could use. I wanted the autopsy to know where the cancer originated. What did it matter? I still wanted to know. For science. For me. For my family. For closure. I didn't ask anyone else. I just told the hospital to do it.

Would knowing where it started change anything? No. She would still be dead.

We left the hospital and did what anyone does after losing a parent. We called the other one. Dad came and we four kids headed out to lunch with him at a cute little restaurant in town near the new mall. We hadn't spent any amount of time all together with him in years. I thought that now that Linda was gone, he would come back to us. Linda had kept us apart. We could be a family again. We could create some nice memories.

"Can you tell us some happy stories about mom?" I asked.

"Like what?"

"Why did you marry her?"

"Oh, I don't know, Nicole."

"Isn't there something nice you can say about her? Anything?"

He couldn't. Or wouldn't. He may have been in shock because he hadn't known how sick she was.

"Dad, it's so nice to be together. I've missed that," I said.

"Well, being together's rather expensive," he replied.

Everyone becomes an orphan if they live long enough. Everyone's parents die, but Dad wasn't dead, hadn't been dead. He was sitting there at the table with us.

But we were motherless.

2000, Montana

AS fast as that, life moved onward. There was admins-trivia to deal with. Funeral home? Burial? Cremation? Urn selection? That would come.

The next day, we piled into Linda's Bronco to go to the funeral home. The owner went to our church. Walt met us there, eyes red. I had never been in a funeral home. I walked into the mid-century building and looked at the dusty blinds. The rest of the place was clean and neat. The funeral director brought out different options for us to choose. An urn, a pamphlet to have at the funeral, an offer to write her obituary, for a fee. There were so many options.

We stood up in unison to pick out her urn. There were wooden ones and metal boxes and all manner of designs. The prices varied accordingly. We quickly settled on a periwinkle ceramic urn. It sat about a foot tall, with a small lid of the same color. The urn's main feature, besides being understated and nondescript, was that it didn't cost much. As instructed, we chose the cheapest of everything.

They asked us if we wanted to see her one last time. I demurred. I had seen Linda for long enough at the hospital. Seeing her again wouldn't change anything.

I also declined to have them write the obituary or print the fliers for the funeral. I would do those things. No need to pay someone to do something I could do.

I wrote a check and we left. Linda paid for her own cremation.

Walt went back to his apartment. The kids and I picked up Gram and then found ourselves in the drive-through for Dairy Queen. The red and white building was at the corner of the two largest roads through our town.

Linda was dead. We thought this every few minutes. No one said it, though.

In the drive-through, I asked what people wanted to eat.

"I want a Blizzard," said John.

"Me too," said Erica.

Gram wanted a hot dog.

"Do you want that to go?" asked the woman through the speaker.

From the back, "Do you want that to go?" said Gram.

Then Montana chimed in, "To go? Do you want that to go?"

We laughed together.

The woman said again, "Do you want that to go?"

"Yes, yes, we want it to go."

"What other option is there?" asked Montana.

Over my shoulder, "Um, we want that to go," shouted John.

More giggling. It felt good to laugh. We hadn't laughed in days, weeks.

We ate in the car, on the go.

At our kitchen table with my laptop, I obsessed about the funeral and the obituary. Linda's good friends would sing. My high school English teacher would do the readings. My church-going years weren't so far behind me that I couldn't choose an appropriate song: *On Eagles' Wings*. I liked the idea of the song. God picks you up and takes you along. I chose the readings with help from Linda's church friends and Father Kevin.

I spent a lot of time on the program for the funeral so that it mirrored the obituary. A great picture of Linda outside her house under a white arbor smiled out at the reader on the cover. Her glasses were on her head. Her white blouse was pressed and she had on her hallmark khaki shorts. You could see her legs and they looked great too. She looked happy, alive.

I put a poem Linda had taped to her mirror about new beginnings and faith on the inside cover.

Dad didn't attend the funeral. He sent a large flower arrangement instead.

Before the ceremony Walt, Erica, and I stood at the front of the church staring at the gigantic arrangement.

"What should we do with these?" Walt asked.

"They seem big," I said.

"Like huge," said Erica.

The flowers were so big they looked inappropriate, as if he were saying that he won, that he was the last man standing.

"Let's move them off to the side. What was he thinking?" I wondered out loud while I moved the flowers.

Perfect Montana summer weather graced the day of the funeral, not too hot or too cool, and sunny with a nice breeze. I hadn't been to a funeral before. It was just like Mass, but a giant picture of my mom stared out at the congregation from the altar. An unexpected mix of people came to the funeral. Old friends and mere acquaintences.

John sobbed through the whole thing. Seeing him so sad was heartbreaking. He physically manifested all our feelings.

The priest told everyone about Linda's grace and how she was now with God. I sat in the pews thinking about my aunt's declaration years earlier when I asked her about what she thought happened when you died. "You're dead, gone. Nothing." Dead. No more. No afterlife. When my aunt said that to me, I felt a black hole in my stomach. I couldn't believe in religion, but equally true was the fact that I couldn't believe that my mother was gone, never to be seen again. The kind priest made me want to believe a little bit. The alternative was just too much to bear.

After the funeral, Linda's friend, Teri, had everyone over for a little party to celebrate Linda's life. There was food outside and I felt loved.

Her obituary ran in the local newspaper, alerting everyone else in the community that my mother was dead.

Two weeks after she died, the sun was streaming in the bay window in the living room when the doorbell rang. The hospital bed was gone. The couches were back where they normally went. The TV had been removed from the living room. Everything was back to normal. The new normal.

When I opened the door, warm summer air streamed into the house. Standing there was a woman Linda knew, a woman I knew. Her ex-husband was a contractor and he had raised the roof on our old house. They had lived way out of town, had grown their own food, and the woman had delivered her six children at home.

With a heavy Boston accent, she said, "Hi, Nicole. I'm here to see your mom."

I knew this was why she was there. I had seen this woman often at the gym. I kept telling her that she needed to come by and see Linda. I had always reported to Linda that this woman said she would come by.

"Oh, well she's gone," I said to the woman.

"When will she be back?"

I took a moment.

"She's not coming back. She's dead."

The woman's face showed shock and then disbelief.

I enjoyed seeing these changes in the woman's face. I felt *schadenfreude*, taking delight in her discomfort.

"What do you mean?" she asked while she touched my arm.

"Come in. Her bed was here for months." I showed her the living room. "Linda kept asking when you were coming by."

We stood there silently in the empty living room.

"I can get you her obituary and the flier from the funeral if you want them."

"Oh, yes, please." Still in shock she wasn't yet crying.

I collected these and handed them to her. The woman looked at the paper.

"Well, I am so sorry. Thank you for these."

I opened the front door and watched as the woman walked to her car on the street.

I contemplated the people who came to visit Linda and those who hadn't. Linda's brother and sister came a few times. My best friend from childhood didn't come. Linda's good friends came from the East Coast. There didn't seem to be any pattern to discern who came versus who didn't come. Some people couldn't afford to come, and some people wanted to remember Linda healthy and well.

I considered Linda's funeral. The church had been full. Our priest spoke lovingly about Linda and her affect on the world. Her tap dancing was brought up. If your life is to be measured in friends, Linda's had been full.

Standing there in the living room after this woman had left, I realized that I needed everyone who knew Linda to know that she was dead in order for it to be real. Until everyone knew, Linda might not be dead because she wasn't dead yet in those people's minds. And then I felt bad about how I treated the woman who showed up to Linda's house, unknowingly.

Later, using the leftover flyers and copies of her obituary, I mailed out death announcements. I used my new calligraphy skills to individually address each envelope to Linda's friends. This felt important at the time. I wanted the envelopes to seem personal, almost like hand-lettered wedding invitations. I sent out a few hundred of these.

For days I called people.

"Hi, this is Nicole Harkin, Linda Harkin's daughter. Yes, she's been sick with cancer. She died." The conversations didn't go much further than that, but I felt I honored Linda. Some friends were surprised. Others had already heard.

There were people I couldn't find. People Linda didn't have in her address book, like her Jewish boyfriend with whom she lived in Chicago before she met Dad. I would have called him too.

Linda's dying was a kind of release. We couldn't have held on much longer. We were stuck in this twilight zone. The stress created by her illness oppressed us. We couldn't move forward with our lives. Even so, I felt guilty because a part of me could breathe a little more.

When I was little, I had gone through Linda's belongings as though they were mine. After Linda died, I went back through her things, crying. Her closet still smelled like her. I could fall into her white blouses hanging there and inhale her scent.

In her closet, there were artifacts of her past life. Her vanity held two jewelry boxes, one covered in cloth from Neiman Marcus and the other leather—obviously from her childhood—and lots of makeup: French makeup and Japanese makeup in small containers. Lots of red lipstick was on hand and many free gifts from Clinique. She had mini-lipsticks too, given out as trials in department stores. Inside the jewelry boxes, there were gold hoop earrings, a snake-shaped bracelet, and rhinestone earrings. Also in the closet were belts. One broken belt in the mix couldn't have been longer than twenty-two inches, with two ivory-colored elephant's interlocking tusks to form the belt buckle. There were also boxes of still wrapped lingerie in there. And her tap shoes.

As a child, I had tried on the elephant belt and imagined being a grown up and glamorous, able to wear any of her clothing. Because Linda was beautiful and my mother, I assumed that I would eventually look like her. Instead of her blond hair, I have dark brown. Instead of her blue eyes, I have brown. I only grew to five-feet-five to her almost six-feet. I never looked any more like her than I ever had. From time to time I tried on the belt. I never told her I broke that belt. How annoying it must have been for her to find out while looking through her stuff that someone had broken her belt.

The vanity became mine now that she was dead. Random bits of her life were lying there in drawers. The stories of where these things came from, who she had been with when she had gotten them, why she kept them for years, were gone. She was gone.

After she was dead, I just needed to get up, get dressed, and be a good example of living for the kids. And, every so often, sit in her closet and breathe.

In the days following the funeral, I woke up and thought "Linda's dead." The hospital bed was gone, the friends were gone, the casserole dishes were still there, but empty, in need of return. I took my showers in the morning now and put actual clothes on instead of the gray onesie. I went on a huge shopping bender. I drove all over the valley we lived in, shopping at antique stores and thrift stores, looking for something. Sometimes I found nothing, but other times I found a set of aluminum cups still in their original antique box, a piece of beautiful fabric, purple and white, hand dyed, and smaller items like a little purple aluminum bowl. I was searching for things that Linda would have liked, that she would have purchased. Shopping was one of the things we did together.

When I was little, every year before school started, we had headed to the mall, just Linda and I. No kids, no distractions, nothing else. I looked forward to these shopping days as much as I looked forward to Christmas. The night before a shopping day, I wouldn't be able to sleep. A kind of possibility existed for the future which made me giddy in anticipation.

We headed downtown early for my new school clothes. She taught me how to shop. First, when entering a store, I assessed the situation. Once I had a firm overview of the store, then I decided where I wanted to go. Dresses? Shoes? Accessories? She said to remember sale items were generally at the back of the section. Go there first. Don't ever pay full price for clothing, she taught. We culled through the items, seeking my size. The chosen items needed to mix and match with at least two other items. This gave me more options in the morning. And don't buy cheap clothing or clothing that's part of a fad because these items weren't worth their price.

At the end, after lunch, if I had been both well behaved and a good shopper—meaning I hadn't spent my entire budget of $200—we went to The Hello Kitty store for new school supplies. The store was a school-aged girl's dream: pencils with cute erasers, calculators in the shape of kitties, and notepads with frogs on them.

But this shopping education was of no use once we had moved to Montana. There the only places Linda went shopping were Costco and The Salvation Army. She liked both places because the inventory was constantly changing. She went to the SA, as we code-named it, every day after she picked the kids up from school. I could reliably find her there in the era before cell phones. They knew her by name there. And if they had something come in they thought she might like, they held it for her.

She shopped around, checking the silver, then the white blouses, and finally, moving on to the sewing section. She found all kinds of cool things there, but she never planned to buy anything. She always left her wallet in the car, so she was forever asking us to go out to the car to get her wallet. When I went there, I told them she was gone, dead. They weren't friends of Linda's, but they were people who had known her—with whom she had interacted daily. I wanted those people to know too, to know where she had gone, why she never came in anymore.

"My mom's dead."

That's how I opened the conversation.

"Linda? She was a tall blond?" said one clerk.

"Oh, of course. We know who you mean. I was sorry to hear that. I saw her obituary in the paper," said the other.

Maybe I wanted more of a reaction. I wanted someone to feel as sad about her death as I did. I kept telling people, looking for that person who felt as sad as me.

A bit further south of town, there was a store called The Stone Chair. I had bought two small leather notebooks there. One was a brown address book and the other a black book with blank pages. I used it to write down the books I had read while Linda was sick. I noted the weather. I didn't use the pages sequentially, preferring to be free spirited and using whatever page I opened to. This minor choice made me feel unconventional, different, better.

Erica and I took Linda's ring to a local jeweler. Linda loved these diamonds and fought for them. She wouldn't have wanted them to just sit in a jewelry box, so we had the diamonds set into new rings. Mine was bezel-set in a platinum men's band, so I could turn it around if I ever felt uncomfortable and wanted to hide the diamond. Erica's was set like an engagement ring, big and proud.

Walt went from our house to his apartment to our house to his apartment, on repeat. He would stop and pick up anything Erica asked for. In the evenings he had a few drinks. He had lost his best friend and lover, but the kids and I weren't able to process his loss with him. We couldn't even name Walt's place in our lives. Progressively he had morphed from Uncle Walter, to Uncle Wawa, and now just Walt. The names denoted his changed position in our family: co-owner, friend, a close friend, family member without a proper title. But when I introduced him, I never had the words to describe his role in our family. He was just Walt.

If Erica hadn't been pregnant, we would have lost Walt soon after Linda, I am sure of it.

A few weeks later, I went back to D.C. to my old life, my old job, and my old apartment. My job had given me a leave of absence and the subtenant in my apartment had moved out. John went back to college a few weeks later. Erica kept working at the movie theater. Walt moved into the basement to help Erica take care of the house.

Dad called me.

"Nicole, Montana needs someone to live with him in Kalispell so he can finish high school. I want you to move back from D.C. to take care of him," Dad said.

"What?" I said.

"I live in Lakeside with my wife. I can't move back to Kalispell." Lakeside is fifteen miles south of Kalispell.

"No, I'm not moving home."

Since I didn't move back to Kalispell, Dad bought a mobile home at the other end of town from Linda's house and that was where Montana lived his last year and a half in high school. Dad insisted Montana live in the mobile home rather than in Linda's house with Erica and Walt, even though Dad was seldom at the mobile home. Montana ended up effectively living on his own. Dad thought Erica was a bad influence, single mom to be that she was.

This just showed how little Dad knew us, especially Erica. The baby had helped Erica get her priorities together. Her grades went up at the community college. She became a pharmacy technician with the goal of getting into pharmacy school. She would have only been a good influence on Montana.

Why wasn't Dad around more? He wasn't working. His wife was still working as a flight attendant at the time, so she was often gone. He sometimes went on trips with her. I don't think he wanted to be around.

Later that year, after Montana had been living on his own for a while in the trailer, I called him. Montana had a girlfriend. They spent a lot of time together. I liked that her family was so nice to Montana. He learned how to cook from her family.

"Any news?"

"I'm graduating early. I figured out I can graduate at the end of this semester."

"A year and a half early? But you're too young."

"High school sucks. I want to be done."

He was only fifteen-years-old.

"Are you sure?"

"Yea, and then I'll just go to college."

His childhood was over. It had ended when Linda died.

Maybe I had made the wrong decision. Maybe I should have moved back to Montana, back home. Montana could have lived with us. He could have finished high school. But I couldn't let Dad dictate my life.

Linda dying from cancer overshadowed everything, and anytime I saw that someone had "valiantly fought cancer" and won, my brain felt like exploding. These stories implied that by sheer force of will, people overcame cancer. But beating cancer or dying from cancer is a flip of the coin. If you're rich or a celebrity, you have a greater likelihood of beating cancer. Think Gloria Vanderbilt, lung cancer twice, and still smoking. If you live near a world-renowned medical center, your odds go way up. Think Mayo Clinic, Johns Hopkins, Cleveland Clinic. Linda lived in the middle of nowhere, had a rare cancer, and what I couldn't see at the time, a death sentence. I felt like the world kept telling me that if she had had the right attitude, the attitude of a fighter, she could have beaten cancer. But that just wasn't true. Linda had been a fighter.

2000, Montana

THE fall after Linda died, we—Walt, the kids, and I—spent the first Thanksgiving without Linda, together. Erica's son, Tanner, had been born just weeks earlier and only three months after Linda died. I had missed it. I hadn't flown back to Montana for his birth.

We can easily remember how long Linda's been dead. She's been dead for as long as Tanner's been alive.

It's funny how often that happens in life. Someone dear dies, and someone dear is born. Are the two connected? What is the universe saying? Of course, we die, but the "when" of dying seems suspiciously not coincidental.

A few days before Thanksgiving, there was a knock at the door. Montana answered it. In came a little army of Linda's church friends with boxes and boxes of food.

"Where should we put the turkey?" asked Mary.

Erica, John, Montana, and I were shocked.

"Oh, Linda had a spare refrigerator in the garage," replied Teri.

Someone carried the turkey out there. A big bag of potatoes, pies, whipping cream, canned veggies, carrots, you name it, arrived. It was all there and on the counter. And as fast as that, they were gone. We just stood there.

The church ladies, however, forgot to leave directions. We had to figure out how to cook Thanksgiving dinner. Since Linda didn't like to cook, she always bought the whole meal fully cooked from the grocery store. She only needed to reheat it the day of.

"Does anyone know how to cook the turkey?" I asked. Walt had actually gone to culinary school after retiring. He knew how to make everything, but wasn't there when all of this transpired. As such, he was in charge of bringing the wine.

"I think my boyfriend does," Erica replied.

"Ok, then he's on the turkey. John, can you make the stuffing?"

169

It came from a box.

"Yes, sure," replied John.

"I'll make the mashed potatoes," I said.

A few days later, we sat down to dinner.

"Is something missing?" I asked.

We looked at the table, with silver goblets and linen tablecloth.

"Where's the veggies?" asked Erica.

The four kids putting on Thanksgiving dinner had forgotten the veggies. That's how it felt, like we were just acting out the holiday. We expected the main characters to appear and with them bring the actual dinner we were supposed to eat.

Since they hadn't shown up, I jumped up and opened a can of green beans, nuked them, and brought them to the table. Voilà, a veggie.

Later that evening we played Pictionary in the basement. The large-screen TV with the scratch still visible sat a bit too close to the couch. The teams were girls vs. boys. The stakes were high and the two sides were well matched. Both teams had to draw this answer at the same time. Then, at the same moment, John and I said the correct answer. French fries! Then we looked at the drawings and laughed hysterically. We'd cheated. Both sides. The golden arches with the letters "mcd" right there as proof on our drawings. No letters were allowed in Pictionary. We couldn't help it. Cheating was genetic.

2001, Washington, D.C. & Montana

I needed to move forward with my life as an example for the kids. I inhabited my responsibility to set a good example for them, years after Linda had told me to do so. Even though Linda felt it was too expensive, I decided to go to law school and I moved to New York.

After her death, I introduced myself like this, "Hi. My name is Nicole Harkin and my mother's dead." I didn't mean for it to happen like that, but I couldn't stop talking. It was kind of an aggressive form of grieving. I wanted everyone to know. I wanted to see their discomfort. It made me feel a little better. People were shocked but kind.

Erica called me crying one morning after I had started law school.

"Nicole, I heard her in the kitchen, outside my room, emptying the dishwasher, making coffee, and having her first cigarette of the day. I got up to see what was happening. She looked fine, but said she wanted to talk to me in her bedroom."

"Who did you hear?" I asked.

"Mom," said Erica.

"Oh, I'm so sorry, honey," I said.

"No, Nicole. I think it was her."

"What did she say?"

"I asked her why she had to leave us and if she was OK. She said it was time for her to go and she was fine. And she said we would be OK too."

Maybe it *was* Linda. I can't disregard that it might have been her. Who knows what happens after death? Linda believed in the Catholic version of the afterlife. She loved us so much, I could imagine her trying to give Erica—us—some peace of mind.

I had a few dreams with Linda too. Sometimes I realized in the dream that she wasn't real. Sometimes, I didn't.

In one dream, Linda drove down the driveway to our house outside of town in Kalispell. She was in an open-topped Jeep—Cream Puff the 1st—

with my grandfather, Mr. Miserable. Mr. Miserable said to me, "See, here she is. She isn't dead."

I looked at Linda and first felt relief and elation. She wasn't dead. But then I realized something was off. It didn't seem like Linda. My grandfather saw my face and said, "OK, so it isn't your mom, but her twin sister. They're just the same."

I knew in the dream that there was no one who was just the same as Linda. When I woke up, lying there in bed, I felt the anguish of her death all over again.

Some time later Montana and I were sitting in the living room. We were talking about religion and God. Montana had been an atheist for awhile. I was telling him how I felt about the existence of God.

Erica walked into the room. "What are you guys talking about?"

"God," said Montana.

"Have you guys accepted Jesus Christ as your Lord and Savior?" Erica asked us with a straight face.

Montana and I looked at each other and laughed. Hard.

"Guys, this isn't funny. If you don't, you're going to hell."

Erica, the woman who had a baby without being married, was lecturing us about going to hell?

Montana and I laughed even harder. And then finally, Erica joined in. I don't know if it was at that exact moment that Erica understood that what she was saying wasn't what she believed, but I know that it happened not too long thereafter.

The four of us represent a wide range of religious beliefs. From an atheist, to an agnostic, to a believer at times, to a fervent believer sometimes. It's strange how we grew up in the same home with the same parents, and yet we don't believe the same things. Are we more Linda or more Dad? More religious or more rational? And do these beliefs change situationally or vary according to our life experiences? I describe our beliefs monolithically. We believe the same things. But that's not quite right. We've taken different lessons from the same experiences, and we describe the same experiences differently. Fundamentally, however, we're good people, despite or because of our beliefs, which might be the more interesting observation.

I felt relieved when I finally stopped telling everyone I met that my mother was dead, but I still had a tendency to tell smokers how she died.

When I started law school I would ask people, "How long have you been smoking? I'm sure you've thought of quitting. Did you know that you can get other cancers besides lung cancer from smoking?"

The random smoker would reply awkwardly because strangers and family members alike had frequently told them, asked them, tried to cajole them to quit.

"My mom died of cancer. It went to her spine and broke it. She couldn't walk."

Sometimes I got a look of horror and sometimes one of dismissal.

I continued anyway.

"Smoking doesn't always kill you in the manner you expect."

I've had some success. I've persuaded one person to quit, a friend from high school.

2003, Montana

DAD still wanted to recover the money he thought Linda owed him. To do so, he sued the trust Linda had set up for us and then wanted $40,000 from the trust to drop his suit. $40,000 was the value of the diamonds that he still felt were his, even though the court had awarded the rings to Linda. The rings were her line in the sand. She would never have given those rings to him, so I had no choice. I couldn't give him my ring.

However, I believe people are more important than things so reconciling my inability to give him the ring required a bit of doublethink. I felt like giving him my ring would have betrayed Linda's memory. At the same time, I longed for a relationship with him.

The four of us were on the phone together one night. Erica called me, and then I called John, and then he looped in Montana. We laughed at being on the phone together. Erica hid until someone said something she couldn't let go by. The conversation turned to Dad and the rings.

"I'm not giving him my ring," said Erica.

"Me either. The only thing we can control is our behavior and how we react to him," I said.

"I'm not giving him mine either. Screw him," said John.

Linda always told me that she viewed her relationship with Dad in terms of a power struggle. Dad wanted control. He controlled their money. He controlled where they lived. She constantly struggled with him to regain some control.

Walt was the executor of Linda's estate and the trustee of our trust. Dad's shenanigans caused him a lot of stress. He wanted Dad to stop harassing us. There was Walt again, steady and reliable, honoring Linda's wish to take care of us. He had morphed yet again into Papa, Tanner's grandfather. Erica, and subsequently all of us, just told people he was our stepfather, a title everyone is familiar with.

"Look, I know this is a lot of money, but your father has assured me that if we give him this money, he'll go away," Walt told us.

"But Walt, when has he ever honored a contract?" I asked.

"This is the best deal I can come up with." Walt's Kentucky twang came out more when he was upset. He wanted $10,000 from each of us.

"But we don't owe him any money," said John.

"Either we give him this money or we waste the money fighting him suing us. This gets him to go away now," said Walt.

It made sense.

I counseled the kids to not engage Dad about the money. I had a mantra with them, "We can't change his behavior, but we can control our responses to his behavior. Becoming angry with him and letting him upset us or divide us lets him win." Win what? Control over our lives. Hearing Linda in my head, I thought this was what he was after.

Some people think the best way to win a power struggle is to let go. So we agreed to Walt's suggestion that we give Dad the money to make him stop suing us.

Then a few weeks later Walt called me to say that Dad brought a new suit, even though we gave him the money.

"I thought you said he had to sign a contract to go away?"

"Now he says Linda still had some of his stuff and he wants it back."

"Like what?"

"His camera and linens."

"Linens? And Linda already gave him his camera. That's it. I'm done. I'm not giving him anything else."

"I'm sorry Nicole. I thought he was done this time." Walt felt bad, but he wasn't to blame. Dad had duped us, again.

I was angry when I hung up the phone. I wanted my parent's divorce to be finished so we could move on with our lives.

Instead, Dad kept filing more briefs with the court. His newest lawyer was willing to let him write his own legal briefs to which the lawyer affixed his name. Dad had gone through three lawyers during the divorce.

Money spent equaled love to Dad. Any time I tried to restart our relationship, things followed the same pattern. He emailed back or answered my calls, but then the conversations always came back to money and whether

I would give him some of Linda's.

I wouldn't, so I stopped calling and emailing.

Then Dad could think in his mind that his kids abandoned him. He could create a story in his head to match his reality.

The court eventually told him to stop filing briefs. He had run out of options.

2003, North Dakota

TIME without Linda went fast and slow. I caught myself thinking, *I can't believe she's been dead for three years*. A friend had asked me how long it was before I felt normal again, how long before I felt like life might go on and I could be happy. That process happened gradually.

In the moments when I could forget that Linda was dead, I felt normal. Those moments became longer and longer. Then it became the large life moments when I most acutely felt the lack of her presence, like when John graduated with honors from college in North Dakota. That same weekend he married his girlfriend.

Erica, Tanner, Montana, Gram, Walt, and I arrived early for the graduation and wedding. We did the things people do for weddings, like a rehearsal dinner and pictures. We expected Dad to just appear—to show up at the last minute.

Dad didn't appear. John was devastated. I was devastated for John. He desperately sought his father's approval, and this seemed like the ultimate rejection.

Dad had always been mean to John. Maybe because they were too much alike? Maybe because John tried so hard to please him? Maybe because Dad was just an ass? Who knows?

2003, Montana

AS time moved on, we were together at irregular intervals. We spoke on the phone often, which was easy, but being in the same house together generated friction between us. We reverted to our immature selves with all of us acting like our inner twelve-year-olds.

The phone rang when I was home visiting Erica.

"Who is it?" I mouthed to Erica.

She scowled back at me, putting her hand over the receiver, "None of your business."

"No seriously, Erica, who is it?"

"You don't pay the bill. It's none of your business."

So I said, "Me, me," sounding like Beaker from the Muppets and left the room.

Each time she started with this selfishness, I said "Me, me" and left. I didn't want to fight, but I did want to convey to Erica that she was being a brat.

Erica's next call was to Dr. T, and we were off to see him.

We sat in his office on the first floor of a building built in the 1960's or 1970's. He sat in his Eames leather recliner. We were on his leather love seat, not wanting to love one another.

Erica told him that I kept saying "Me, me" when I was upset with her.

He nodded his head and said nothing. He had a habit of that, and it could be rather unnerving. I couldn't tell if he approved or disapproved of what was said, which was the point, I suppose.

Then Erica launched into another story about something that I had done in the week or so that I had been home. How could her laundry list of my abhorrent behaviors have gotten so long so fast?

More nodding from Dr. T.

Finally, she told him I had asked her who was on the phone. At the end of her tale of woe, she asked him what he thought.

He paused and then said, "Me, me."

For two milliseconds Erica looked as though she was going to kill the man, and then we laughed. I later learned that in Chinese, *Meimei* means little sister. Perfect.

After Linda died, Dr. T became a mediator for us. He gave us tools that helped us function together and taught us to like each other. He listened to the stories of our fights and offered up some nuggets of insight. He never sent us a bill.

He taught us about the "the apology eraser." We would have a huge fight. Then we separated from each other to cool down. When we came back together, I might say something like, "John, I'm sorry I screamed at you, but you were being such an ass."

Everything from the "but" on erased my apology. Either I was sorry or I wasn't. If I wanted to keep fighting, I could do that too, but I shouldn't mix up the two. In order to apologize, I had to stop at "I'm sorry." Sometimes we needed to realize that the fight needed more time to resolve.

He also told us, as we came in with jumbled up messes of stories about fights, to make sure that we knew what it was we were fighting about and to fight about one thing at a time.

"Nicole hogs the washer and dryer when she is home, she owes me thirty-dollars for all the food she eats when she's here, and she always wants to know what I'm doing."

Nothing would be resolved in that fight. There was just too much to rationally unpack it when we were upset.

Another tool was "Don't give your opinion or advice unless your family member asks for your advice or opinion." As the oldest, I was guilty of this one. For example, Erica called me, all upset about her boyfriend breaking up with her. I listened and then offered that she was better off without that loser. I never liked him anyway. I went on to mention that she should change her passwords and get new keys to the house.

That's when the fighting erupted. Erica didn't want advice, she wanted a sympathetic ear. And, she and he might not be finished. So unless Erica asked me what to do—asked for my advice—then I should keep my mouth shut. But once Erica asked, it was game on. I was free to tell her what I thought, but if I wanted to remain on good terms with my family, I shouldn't tell unless asked. And conversely, she couldn't be angry with me for giving her my honest opinion once she asked.

Anytime we were together, we kept calling Dr. T in desperation, crying to his secretary and asking for an appointment. We were happy to see each other but then we'd start fighting. We needed him to help us, and he did.

With Linda dead and Dad out of the picture, without these tools, we had almost no chance of remaining close. Dr. T helped us to figure out what we were fighting about: our sadness at our losses, our loss of Linda, our loss of our family, and our loss of stability. In helping us recognize that we were processing our sadness when we were fighting, he helped us heal. He could have seen our bickering as entitled little brats unable to get along, but it was more than that. Our fighting came from years of patterned behavior in which we learned from Dad and Linda to scream and yell at each other rather than talk about what was happening. Our family had been slowly tilting ever on a course to capsize. He gave us the chance to right the ship, as it were. Even without Linda and Dad, we could choose to be a functioning family.

2005, Washington, D.C. & Montana

FIVE years after Linda died, John wanted us to sell the house.

Conference calls were held. John wanted his share of the value of the house to buy his own, but Erica still lived there.

I argued that our keeping the house was financially advantageous because the value of the house kept increasing with every year.

Montana kept quiet.

After many more hours on the phone, Erica decided to buy John out of his portion of the house. John got a lawyer and had us sign an agreement. More lawyers. More annoyance. More money spent on lawyers. Erica, Montana, and I weren't pleased. Finally, it was done and then the contents of the house needed to be divided up.

"I don't want any of Mom's stuff anyway," said Erica.

"I think you should keep the couches. They're nice," I said.

"I don't want them."

A few weeks later, after pricing couches, Erica changed her tune. "I want the couches. Couches *are* expensive," she told me.

The day arrived to split up everything. Erica, John, Montana, and a neutral third-party—who just happened to be one of my honors English teacher from high school, who also didn't remember me—met at the house in Montana. During summer break from law school, I was house sitting in the middle of nowhere Virginia. I sat in the house's hot tub reading *The Last Samurai* in between calls from Erica. I couldn't handle dividing up Linda's possessions. If Linda didn't have her house intact, then she couldn't come home. So I gave Erica the list of things I wanted from the house, and I was on the phone for the round-robin picking of items.

I wanted our dishes, our family table, and the art in the house. Erica and Montana wanted other things.

"John's driving us nuts," said Erica on the phone.

"What does he want?"

"Everything. He just used his turn to take the plunger in the bathroom."

"Humm. Does he realize you are still living there?" I asked.

"I'm not sure. Now I am choosing things that I don't care about just because he keeps doing the same."

"What does the lady directing things say?"

"Even she's annoyed. And we're paying her, so the longer this takes, the more she gets paid."

John couldn't help himself. He tried to pick the towels, the toilet paper dispenser, and other things that were just strange. This was part of his grieving. He was trying to keep his Mom by keeping her things.

John disregarded Linda's instructions about some items, like the silver. He picked the silver in one of his turns, and then the silver goblets.

"But, John, Mom wanted us to divide those up," said Erica.

"I don't believe it. How do I know what Nicole wrote on that piece of paper was really what Mom wanted? She didn't sign it. I picked the silver," he said.

"But John, come on," said Erica.

No one could dissuade him and the process was already too emotionally taxing to fight. Linda didn't like it when we fought, so the silver was his.

In John's world, it was take, lest ye be taken. So he took and took and took.

Erica, Montana, and I always tried to return this behavior with love.

2007, Pittsburg, PA

LINDA had been dead for seven years when Montana married in Pittsburgh.

Standing in the lobby of the hotel where the ceremony was to take place, Erica and I watched as Dad and his wife walked in. I hadn't seen or spoken to him since her death.

He looked old. Did he think that when he saw me too? I was fluent in German, having spent two years in Germany on two different fellowships. I'd passed the bar exam and established my career. My high school crush, Brent, and I had reconnected years later and now we lived together in Washington, D.C. I was an adult. But the moment I saw Dad I felt like a nervous child again.

Dad had a slight limp from his strokes all those years ago. His hair was thin and gray. He looked gaunt but still had his belly.

"Hey, kids, how are you doing?"

"Hi, Dad."

Anyone walking by could tell we were his children. The nose was the same. The lips were the same. The hair was the same. And yet, we were greeting each other like strangers. I didn't know how to interact with him.

I wanted him to hug me and have him tell me how much he had missed me. And, I wanted him to apologize to me. He didn't do any of these things. Erica and I headed upstairs on the elevator. I felt his wife glaring at me.

The picture from Montana's wedding of the whole family is awkward. Dad and his wife, the four kids, Montana's new wife, John's wife, my boyfriend, Walt, Gram, Tanner, all standing next to one another as if we were a close family, as though we liked each other. Dad had only met Tanner a few times, and only for short periods. And the rest of us, save Montana, didn't talk to Dad either. We were a family in picture only.

At the reception, Dad and his wife sat with Montana and everyone else sat together at a different table. There was some mingling. I desperately wanted to talk to my Dad. I missed him. I wanted him to tell me he was proud of my Fulbright Fellowship to Germany and my law degree. I wanted him to take an interest in my boyfriend and tell me how much he missed me. After dinner, I sat down with him at the round table with a white tablecloth. Montana and his friends played interactive video games.

The wedding flowers in vases were on the table with remnants of wedding cake.

Nothing was said. The silence hurt. His wife got up and left the table.

"What are you up to these days?"

"Working for the government. How have you been?"

The conversation sounded like that of strangers meeting, a bit strained.

"Dad, can't we get along? Why do we have to keep fighting?"

"Just give me the ring. Then things would be fine."

I touched my finger with the ring on it. I looked around. Walt was there, at a different table. Linda's friend, Carol, and her husband, Don were there. Montana's friends from childhood were there. Tanner played the Wii video games. Linda wasn't there. Things were the same, but different.

"I'll check on Brent and see what he's up to."

My sadness overwhelmed my sense of happiness for Montana and his new wife. I just wanted us to get along.

That was what Montana wanted too and he was better at achieving this goal. "Never rock the boat" could be his motto regarding our family. Conflict avoidance or serenity achievement? Who can say? Either way, he had a relationship with everyone.

2008, Washington State

DAD had almost died twelve years earlier. Linda had been dead for eight years. Brent and I were finally marrying.

After all these years, Brent finally fell in love with me and then things happened quickly. We moved in together. He and I had spent Christmas and New Year's apart, and over that time he decided to ask me to marry him. In the airport corridor, he came right up to me and got down on one knee. I was so embarrassed, I said, "Yes, yes. Just get up!" We decided to marry in Portland because Brent's dad lived there and wasn't able to travel.

When Brent asked me to marry him, we had called Walt together to tell him. No one discussed calling Dad. I wanted Dad to come to our wedding, but I didn't expect him to.

But three months before my wedding, he instant messaged me at work. A screen popped up from him.

Hey, what's up?

Busy that day, I saw it was a message from Dad. I panicked and quickly closed the browser.

A few minutes later, I re-opened the browser window. Up popped the instant messenger again.

Are you there? It's Dad.

Torn between curiosity and the need for control, I didn't know how to respond.

Muppet, I heard you are getting married. I want to talk to you about the wedding. Can you chat?

I closed the browser again and sent him an email telling him I couldn't talk. I would call him later. He emailed me back, telling me he understood that I was busy and wanted to talk about his role in my wedding.

A week later Montana called me at work. Montana never called me, and especially not at work.

"What's up?"

He was on the west coast. It was early for him to be calling.

"Uncle Frankie just called. Dad had a heart attack."

I cried but stayed calm.

"How bad is it?"

"Very bad. You need to come to Spokane."

"What happened?"

"He was drinking some milk and his heart stopped."

I hung up and walked to my boss's office. I worked in government as an oversight analyst. I had only been at the job for a few months. In tears, I told him I needed to leave.

"Are you close to your father?" he asked.

"We don't talk, but I need to go."

"Take as much time as you need."

Maybe it wasn't as bad as Montana said, I hoped.

I called Brent. He told me to get on a plane. Erica and John were already on their way to Dad when I reached them.

On the flight, I imagined the scene of his heart attack in his Washington home. I replayed the image in my head, over and over.

Dad had arrived home from gliding in New Mexico. He couldn't fly airplanes but he could fly gliders, the next best thing. He hadn't felt great and bought a plane ticket to fly home, something a retired commercial pilot was loath to do. Once home, he was tired, but he headed downstairs to his office and checked his email. He still had his large credenza. He showered before bed.

As he was lying in the bed, he decided to get up and go to the kitchen. He had gotten himself a tall glass of milk with ice. The ice was key. Drinking milk without ice leads to drinking lukewarm milk, and that never makes anyone feel better.

He drank the milk. The ice clinked in the glass as the milk emptied.

Sometimes, when I imagine places, I get mixed up. I conjured a picture in my head of how I expected his house to look. It was a log cabin home. His bedroom was upstairs from the kitchen. The furniture was dark and the whole house was dark, too. In my conjured scene, I looked down on him from the upstairs as he sat on a chair next to the kitchen counter. One light illuminated him as he sat there, almost like he was on stage. I had, however, never been to the house he was living in with his wife.

In my imagined scene, Dad finished his glass of milk. He might have noticed as he was swallowing that his heart felt weird, but his heart felt weird a lot of the time.

And then his wife heard something in the kitchen.

When she arrived in the kitchen, Dad was having a heart attack. In her rendition of the story, she pulled him off the chair. She called 911 and did CPR. I can imagine the dilemma she faced: do nothing for Dad and call 911 first, or start CPR and somehow call 911 during CPR. In CPR training, they tell you to tell someone else to call 911, supposing you won't be alone. His brain went without oxygen for fifteen minutes while the EMTs drove to their house in the middle of nowhere. On their last try, they restarted his heart.

The doctors had super-cooled his body in the hopes that they could save his brain. During his last coma, they hadn't had this technology. They didn't know to super-cool him to save his brain. That time we were just lucky.

This time, as Erica, John, Montana, and I waited in the hospital for Dad to recover or die, things were different. Dad's wife was calling the shots. She was the one sitting by his bedside. She didn't have to sneak around. She didn't invite me to dinner with her. She didn't look at me. She didn't address me or ask my opinion about things. She wasn't nice to me.

Pilots die of heart attacks in large numbers. The official reason given for their mandatory retirement age is because of decreased faculties, but my brother John said it's because pilots don't live long after age sixty-five. There is a physical toll to flying commercial airplanes because of pilot's increased radiation exposure from flying. Proximity to the sun matters, over time, and Dad had already almost died once. He was now sixty-eight.

The doctors waited to see if Dad would wake up. As he lay in the hospital, occasionally his body shuddered, or he moved his head. The movements seemed intentional. The nurses explained that his movements seemed intentional because of the damage to Dad's brain stem.

Erica, John, and Montana were staying at his house with his wife. I was staying at a hotel near the hospital since I had not been invited to stay at Dad's house. One day, after we were there a few days, Erica needed something that was at the house, so Erica, John, and I drove out to Dad's house.

His real house was much different than the imagined house. The real house was much smaller and airier. You could almost see out to the kitchen from the bedroom. There were no chairs in the kitchen, just a pair of stools off a peninsula between the kitchen and dining room. The dining room table looked cheap, but seated six, just as our family table had. The cabinets were white.

I looked around the downstairs. There was a wall of videotapes organized in brown cases and Dad's credenza. These were our family home videos. Pictures of the airplanes he had flown decorated the walls. It was a man-cave with a big-screen TV.

I opened the credenza desk drawers. It looked the same as it had years ago when I had wanted to see what was in Dad's desk. I had wanted to be close to this man who graced us with his presence every other week. He had kept interesting things in his desk: it held the keys to who he was. His desk had been off-limits. In fact, the drawers had seemed to be locked at first, but as I had learned as a child, if I pulled out the middle drawer, all of the other drawers unlocked. Nifty.

The phone kept ringing and announcing who was calling. "Unknown caller" it kept repeating. No one answered the calls. It wasn't our home. Dad's wallet was sitting on his desk. I opened it and was surprised to find pictures of me in it. Pictures of Linda and me from when I was just two-years-old. There was another picture of our whole family taken on the occasion of my high school graduation. The pictures were worn and dirty, but they were there.

After we were there for a few minutes, a neighbor came over. Erica spoke to him.

"Is Nicole here?" he asked.

"What?" asked Erica.

"You dad's wife just called me and asked me to come over to tell you that Nicole isn't allowed to go in the house."

I heard the commotion and went upstairs.

"I'm Nicole," I said.

"Well, would you mind leaving? Your dad's wife seemed a bit crazed."

I walked out of the house with tears running down my face. I was mad. Erica was mad too. So were John and Montana. This moment wasn't the time to behave like that.

And why did she dislike me so much? Hate me, even? I assume that she wanted me to repay her the money Dad had borrowed from her for my semester of college. I never asked her. I didn't want to have a relationship with her. I didn't like her. I didn't like how she catered to my Dad's every whim, waiting on him hand and foot. Dad had tried to tell me how wonderful she was, how she had left her abusive husband with nothing and learned English, how smart she was. But at the bottom of it all, she wasn't my mother. He had picked someone else, and not unlike Linda, I couldn't get past that. Montana could, John could sometimes, but Erica couldn't really either.

So I sat in the car until the kids were ready to go back to the hospital.

"I can't believe she did that," I said while still crying.

"Me either," said Erica through tears as she drove.

Dad had needed to have a pacemaker installed in his heart. He had refused to do so only a few months earlier. Maybe he was scared of more surgery, more time in a hospital. Or maybe he was worried he wouldn't sufficiently recover to fly gliders, his *ersatz* activity. He had a $100,000 glider parked in the Southwest. That's where he had been.

The doctors again told us that Dad was brain-dead, but this time the doctors were correct. His brain had gone without oxygen for too long while the ambulance raced its way out of town to his house, his wife beating on his chest. She was forced into the same position Linda had been in, pull the plug or not? If she didn't, then she could end up spending every dollar she had keeping him on life-support. But he might miraculously recover. It had happened before. Or she could listen to the doctors.

Dad had been an organ donor for years. I was a donor because I remembered how strongly he felt about it.

She decided to remove life-support after it was clear that he was dead. His wife didn't let them harvest any organs. Not even his corneas. His body was wasted, and he was dead.

John, Erica, Montana and I went with Dad's wife to plan the funeral. The funeral home was silent while the funeral director asked us what kind of urn we wanted. I kept quiet. His wife was having problems making decisions.

"Do you want us to do this with you?" Montana kindly asked Dad's wife.

He probed her interest in different urns and helped explain or interpret what the funeral director was asking. His soft voice emanated patience.

"Do you want to see your father's body?" the funeral director asked.

"No, I don't," I replied.

"Yes," said Montana, Erica, and John.

"Come on, Nicole," said Montana.

The swinging doors allowed me to see into the room where his body was without stepping into the room. I could see them standing around him. I didn't want to get closer.

"Come on. You need to see him one last time," said Erica.

I didn't go in. I couldn't handle it.

From the door, I looked at his body on the gurney, lying there.

I didn't have any clothes suitable for a funeral so we went shopping. I found pants and a coat and shoes and then eyed two gray pillows with artful loops near the checkout. I bought these too.

"How are you going to take these pillows home?" asked Erica.

"I can check them. I don't care. I want them."

The funeral itself was dismal, the opposite of Linda's funeral. Looking around as I read some words about Dad, it was clear that he didn't have many friends. His lawyer was there. His best friend from Georgia didn't come. Walt was in Spokane to help us but stayed at the hotel during the funeral. The people there were my family, a friend of mine, Dad's brother and wife, and that was it.

Dad drank one last glass of milk. He loved milk. I love milk. And then he had a heart attack.

I have an easy way to remember how long Dad's been dead. It's as long as I have been married because my wedding was a mere six weeks after he died. Walt walked me down the aisle in his best dress kilt.

Dad had the heart attack a week after he had emailed me back.

The fact that he tried to contact me racked me with guilt. He had finally wanted to talk to me and I had felt too overwhelmed to respond.

I searched and searched my email and deleted items to find these last emails between us, when he told me it was OK that I hadn't chatted with him at work. It was OK that I had been too busy to talk to him. He understood. He had indeed emailed me these things, but I couldn't find the evidence. I couldn't locate the actual electronic communications. Like him, they were just there and then gone.

Your parent's relationship affects how you see relationships, but we don't know how exactly it will affect those relationships.

One day, Brent casually suggested as we were walking to work one blustery winter morning that we start washing our laundry separately.

"What?" I replied.

"That way I can make sure I take my wrinkle-free shirts out as soon as the dryer stops."

"What are you saying? You don't want to do your laundry with mine?"

I was in hysterics on the sidewalk of Massachusetts Avenue in Washington, D.C. at 8:15 in the morning. People were noticing.

"I just thought it might be easier. Then you wouldn't have to worry about it," he said.

"So you don't want to be with me?"

"How did you get from my asking about separate laundry to separation?" he asked.

We walked in silence. I realized that the separate laundry story had marked, in my head at least, the beginning of the beginning of the end of my parents' relationship. Dad had criticized Linda's laundry abilities and that had been it. She stopped washing his laundry. *Finito.* It took twenty-five more years for their relationship to end, but still. They couldn't even figure out how to do the laundry together, so of course, they would eventually divorce.

"Let's just do our laundry together," Brent said. "Unwrinkled shirts don't mean as much to me as you do."

Dad had spent a lot of time threatening to take us out of his will. His wife had been required to file the will if one existed and he had an estate of any value, but she never filed a will with the Court.

Erica, John, Montana, and I called a lawyer. We discussed options. We thought about suing to get his wife to file the will.

My uncle had a copy of the will, but he refused to give us a copy and he urged us not to press it. I think he thought the contents of the will would upset us. Maybe he didn't agree with how Dad had chosen to write his will. I expect Dad had explicitly written us out of his will.

And ultimately, we decided not to sue. We didn't want to continue the pattern of suing people. We don't know and won't ever know, if he had indeed written us out of his will. Suing someone takes fighting to the next level. Suing is stressful and expensive. Life's short. We didn't want to waste any more time in court, on him. We chose to press on.

I think Dad had realized he wasn't living the authentic life that he wanted to live when he woke up from the coma following his staph infection. He wasn't happy, hadn't been happy, for a long time. So he decided to change his life. Unfortunately, his changed life didn't leave any room for me.

Living a dual life must have been exhausting for him as well. Essentially he had two wives.

I can't help but feel angry with him for making the choice to go live his alternate life rather than work things out with us. I had this notion that he would go live with his girlfriend, and then have this realization that he made the wrong choice. Either his girlfriend would tire of taking care of him and leave him, or he would miss us and our family. I honestly felt things would go back to the way they were before—eventually.

Changing his life also had a perverse impact on me. Dad made radical changes late in his life. He showed us that this was possible. We have the power to change our situation, no matter the cost or difficulty. So many parents never make the change and die unhappy. Choices.

Today - Ending

FOR fifteen years, Linda sat on Erica's mantel.

"What's in that pretty vase on your mantle?" visitors asked. The purple container was pleasing to look at.

"My mom."

Erica took a little glee from shocking people with this fact. The urn was indeed attractive.

Linda was on Erica's mantel because of a family impasse.

"Guys, we need to sprinkle Linda's ashes," Erica said on the phone with the four of us.

"I know. But I don't want John to fly her over Glacier National Park. I'm worried he will be too upset and crash."

I also imagined the ashes flying back into our faces and us inhaling Linda.

"I'm a professional, Nicole. I won't crash. I do this for a living," John said.

"But still. I don't think it's a good idea."

Montana just chuckled at our ongoing conversation.

Again we tabled sprinkling her.

But now Erica was finally moving out of Montana. She was the last one of us living there, and she was done with pharmacy school. We needed to honor this last request by Linda.

We planned a weekend of camping in Glacier Park to do it. We brought tents and sleeping bags, we cooked over a fire, and then we rented two boats on a clear chilly summer morning.

To document the event I brought my Polaroid camera. John drove one boat with his wife and Walt. Erica, Tanner, Montana's wife, and I were in the other boat piloted by Montana. We rode out twenty minutes to the middle of Lake McDonald. We hadn't been boating together since we were little.

When we found the right spot, we tethered the boats together. There was a bit of wind. The glacial water was freezing, as it always was. We each said a few words but uttered no prayers.

Erica opened the urn and started sprinkling. And sprinkling. And sprinkling.

"There was more of Linda than I realized," she said.

We laughed. And it was true.

I have often imagined what life might have held had Dad died the first time he was sick. My parents would have never divorced and a whole mythology surrounding their relationship would have emerged—a happy story. They met flying and our family had been perfect. Remember the trip to Legoland? Or watching him bass fish on the lake? He had such a love of life. How he took us skiing every weekend? He was so much fun. Gone would be the memories of having to choose between giving him my mother's diamond ring or having a relationship with him.

I don't regret not giving him the ring, because even if I had given it to him, there always would have been something else. Something else to try to control my behavior with.

If Dad had died, Linda would have taken charge of our finances. She would have sold the house and the extra cars. Maybe the kids would have resented her for living and having made the hard choice to take Dad off life support. I doubt I would have finished school at my large university. Too expensive, Linda would have said because she had three more children to educate.

What if Linda hadn't died? Would Linda have moved? Would Linda have married Walt? Would Gram and Linda have talked to each other again? Would Erica have had Tanner? Would Linda have stopped smoking and never gotten cancer? Would I have felt greater sadness that Dad was dead?

In either outcome, I am sure that Linda would have gotten cancer, and she would be dead now. Both of my parents would still be dead, just in a different order.

I had saved Linda's diaries that she kept while she and Dad were divorcing. They sat in my various closets. And then, the diaries were nowhere to be found. Gone. Lost in a move. I tore my apartment apart looking for their metal case with a black plastic handle.

Maybe I lost the box on purpose. Reading about how much Linda hated Dad was hard. "Hated." Anytime we used that word as children, Linda stopped us. "Hate is a very strong word. Are you sure that you feel that way?" No other language merited comment. Her admonishment runs through my head every time I read or use that word. No, she didn't hate him. She loved him and hated his behavior.

Sprinkling her ashes had been sad, but not as sad as I expected. It felt more like the completion of an important task. Losing her diaries left me bereft. I had lost my mom's thoughts.

Years later I called the hospital pathologist where Linda had been treated. Linda's autopsy had originally come back inconclusive and I wondered if they could tell me more now. Maybe the science had advanced over the years. Maybe what she had was HPV—human papillomavirus—and that had caused her cancer.

The new hospital pathologist offered to look again at her slides for clues to the origins of her cancer. Surprisingly, they still had Linda's slides. Even fifteen years later the tissues yielded no more answers. The doctor couldn't tell me anything new.

We do know she smoked, a lot. She drank, a fair bit, but only wine. She was under extreme stress from the divorce, and she had that horrible flu just before the cancer grew on her neck.

I think it was the flu. Her body wasn't able to fight off the flu. Tasked with the flu and fighting the random cancer fires that must have constantly flared up in her system, her immune system was just overrun. The flu had tipped the scales.

The cancer came from all of these things, and from none of them. It had just happened.

What I do know is that I regret three things during Linda's illness: not getting her to smoke pot, not allowing her to smoke cigarettes, and not stopping her treatment earlier—or maybe even starting her treatment in the first place. I bet Linda would have loved the pot. I am certain now she had smoked pot before, even though she denied it. Linda wouldn't have smoked pot in her house, though, because she would have been worried about the example it would have set for Montana, as well as for the rest of us.

Then, however, even less than now, no one mentioned that you might choose not to have any treatment for your cancer—no chemo, no radiation— in favor of a higher quality of life at the end. Had I been older, and wiser, able to hear what the doctors were telling us—that Linda would be dead in six months—I would have urged Linda to make different choices. We would have foregone chemo and radiation.

I was sitting outside of a coffee shop in Washington, D.C., where I lived and a woman behind me was telling her friend how she had squamous cell cancer growing on her neck. The doctor had wanted to do radiation, she told her friend. She said the doctor wasn't too worried about that kind of cancer, but she, herself, was worried about her sex life if the cancer had in fact been caused by HPV. In my head, I was screaming at this woman because she was talking about this in public, because she sat behind me, because I felt like I knew how her story would end. I was screaming at the universe—by which I mean at God—for putting her behind me. What were the odds of her sitting behind me?

I had to turn around and look at her. After seeing her, I kept wondering about her sex life. She looked normal, average, mousy, boring, not like someone I expected to have a rip-roaring sex life.

Instead of engaging her—and telling her *that* cancer had killed my mom—I got up and moved to a different table. I couldn't deal with listening to her. I called Erica and told her everything.

"That's strange. Did you say anything to her? What did she look like?"

"No, I just moved. She wasn't cute, but who am I to judge?"

"I would have moved too."

Cancer seems like a curse. It's foisted upon you because of something you did.

Linda had been so upset about the divorce, and she was such a believer in God. I can't imagine reconciling the thought that God never gave anyone more than they could handle, and yet Linda became so sick after almost losing everything. It seemed like God had doubled down on Linda, on us.

I don't believe in religion in the same way that I don't believe in traffic. Why can't the people in the front just go faster? Why do I need a religion with people telling me what to believe, think, and feel in order to believe in some unknowable creator?

But I do believe in some higher power, entity, something out there, because what's the alternative?

I will never see Linda again. That seems like too much to bear. I can't fully comprehend that I won't ever hear her make that "chu" sound again when told something she doesn't quite believe. So, to that end, belief in something else is a coping mechanism for me. If there is some chance that I might see her again, then I can press on. I can work it out. I can live.

Dad had lived. I felt as though I had a hand in that. I had gotten through to the universe. I had thought I could do the same thing for Linda.

Now, what I sometimes think is that in asking for Dad to be saved, I shortened Linda's life in exchange. Rationally, I know this isn't the case. I understand this, but I still wonder about the universe and how my requests or intentions affect the future, whether my intentions matter. Maybe you only get one answered prayer in your life, one miracle.

I don't know the answer. We can't know the answer, but if someone had said to me, "Nicole, I will save your Dad, but that will mean that Linda will die earlier," I don't know how I would have responded. In the middle of a crisis, you want to get through that crisis. Other future crises are put off. I would have made the deal with the thought that I could re-negotiate before the next deadline.

I know this is just magical thinking.

She died. I did everything I could do to get her to stop smoking, and then I got the best health care for her once she was sick. I was there for her through everything.

Regardless of any of my actions, she would still be dead today. I didn't make a bargain with the universe or the devil. I didn't save my Dad. And luckily, I never had to choose between either of their lives. That was done for us.

These experiences of death have lasting effects. I am constantly aware that I could die anytime, and now, even more so, since having children. I am aware that any moment could be the last "before moments," before everything changes. Walking down the street, I imagine that a driver could hop the curb and run me over. A widow maker could fall out of a tree, killing me on the sidewalk. I could be struck by lighting. I could slip in the shower and die. I could have cancer.

Many people get cancer. I may, in fact, get cancer in my life. The scariest part of Linda's cancer remains the unknown. We will never know where it began, so any small malady in me could be the beginning. But I never smoked and I don't drink—often.

I remember the time, though, that I almost killed Montana, John, and I in Linda's last Suburban. The SUV was brand new and had been specially ordered with gray leather seats and all the extras. Linda had waited for six months for that SUV to arrive. Coming home from town one evening before we had lost the house, but after Dad had been sick, it somehow came up that a car couldn't be shifted into "reverse" while it was in motion.

"Yes, you can, Nicole," said John.

"No, to change gears on all new cars you need to have your foot on the brake."

"No. You're wrong."

In the way that only siblings can try to demonstrate to one another that they're correct, I attempted to change gears at fifty-five miles per hour.

The SUV was instantly swerving and up on two wheels. Putting a half-ton vehicle onto two wheels is a feat. I yanked the steering wheel back the other direction and we went up onto the other two wheels. I pumped the brakes, we slowed and I felt the four wheels hit the ground. I put it into drive and we went home in silence. When I parked it in the garage, I swore the boys to secrecy.

The next morning, Linda couldn't get it to back out of the garage. The car dealer was called. The SUV was towed to the dealership. A new vehicle was ordered to replace it, because everyone but John, Montana, and I thought this one had a lemon transmission.

I was lucky. Very very lucky.

Even while watching for death to show up, I'm still not a naturally negative person. I expect to find a parking space in front of every place I go, and there is a space there seventy-five percent of the time. The rest of the time the space I find is a block up. I expect everything to always work out, and it largely does.

Linda died just before Tanner was born. Thank God Erica didn't listen to me. She chose to have him. I was so vehemently determined that Erica shouldn't have the baby. I was so wrong. Tanner brought new life into our family: Walt had someone to take care of, Erica had a reason to finish school, and we had someone to lavish love upon. Tanner helped create new happy memories for us.

I called Erica early one morning. "Erica, I'm so sorry. I was so wrong. I was so horrible to you when you were pregnant."

"I know. And you didn't even come out when I had Tanner." Erica was still mostly asleep, but she managed to remember this detail.

"I just didn't know. I thought I knew. I didn't, though."

That's such a large part of growing up: Realizing you don't know everything, can't know everything.

"Nicole, it's ok. You've been there for me ever since."

Tanner is blond with blue eyes, just like Linda. He's stubborn in the same way she was. And like her, you should never think of asking to share any food with him. He doesn't like to share.

One morning, I woke up and read my email with a coffee sitting on the desk next to me. There was an email from John.

"Guys, I wanted to tell you that I listened to the recordings I made while we were dividing up Mom's house. I was a real jerk and I'm sorry."

I couldn't believe that John had recorded our calls. And I couldn't believe he had apologized. John's behavior at the time had me worried that he was becoming more and more like Dad, and that wasn't a good thing. This email was proof that he wasn't becoming Dad. He could listen to himself with a bit of space, learning and growing. He could change.

After thinking about it, I decided it was a good thing that he recorded the calls. I remembered that he was difficult during that period, but part of my resiliency comes from my poor memories of negative events. My brain just presses on.

We were quick to forgive John. With our parents gone, we lacked an ultimate arbiter and got over things quickly. Besides, someone could die, we know too well, so it was better to just get along than fight. We had finally stopped fighting, as Linda had implored us to.

Today John and his family live in Idaho with their three kids. He owns a fly-fishing company and is a commercial pilot. Erica lives in Washington State with Tanner and Walt. She's married. I love telling people my sister is the pharmacist in the small town where she lives. Walt is retired and does whatever he wants, so long as Erica's errands are done first. Montana lives with his wife and two daughters in Seattle. He works as a computer engineer. Until recently, Gram lived in St. Louis, alone. At ninety-two she had to move but remains ever independent.

We're OK. We must press on.

While looking through some slips of paper and other detritus from life, I found a note from Linda, "To Nicole, who can do anything she works hard to do." She wrote down that message, but she also told me that often, as did

Dad. I have a book he gave me when I graduated from high school: *Letters to Your Daughter*. The beige covered book is cheesy and full of platitudes, but inside the cover he wrote me a note telling me I could achieve anything I set my mind to.

They had a message. And for all of their other faults, they had parented us well together.

Thanks

I'M just going to leave you with a list of the people who helped me write this book. I appreciate them.

First, my family: Brent Lattin, John Harkin, Erica Harkin, Montana Harkin, Eve Murry, Walter Whitfield, Carol Gordon, Kate Harris, and Ed Epping.

And in alphabetical order: Jessica Baggenstos, Danielle Brian, Jen Brown, Amy Clark, Nicole Coomber, Marcus Corbin, Karen Davison, David DeRosa, Carol Fordonski, Stephanie Haggerty, Teri Iwerson, Mark Jacobsen, Bobbie Kandarian, Maureen Kaiser, Joyce Koffler, Steve Lympus, Claudia Männel, Kim Ochs, Mary Lloyd, Laura Partridge-Lympus, John Perryman, Tania Ralli, Terri Rusconi, Keith and Pam Rutter, Glenn Simpson, Laura Sliter, Emily Smith Goering, Nancy Ross, Nicole Sullivan, Stacey Swann, Haylie Swenson, Dana Tompkins, and Opal Winebrenner.

And all of my other friends and anyone I left out: thank you.

To the faculty and other participants of the Stanford Online Writer's Studio, many thanks.

And finally, a heartfelt thank you to Dr. T.

About the Author

Nicole Harkin currently resides in Washington, D.C. with her husband and two small children. She works as a writer and family photographer. As a Fulbright Scholar during law school, Nicole lived in Berlin, Germany where she studied German environmentalism. Her work can be found in *Thought Collection* and *you are here: The Journal of Creative Geography*. She is currently working on mystery set in Berlin.

View other Black Rose Writing titles at www.blackrosewriting.com/books

and use promo code **PRINT** to receive a **20% discount** when purchasing.

BLACK ROSE
writing™

Made in the USA
Middletown, DE
31 August 2021